Let's begin your GOGI journey...

Getting Out by Going In • P.O. Box 88969 • Los Angeles, CA 90009
www.gettingoutbygoingin.org

Teach Me How To Gogi

Teach me how to gogi, Thats what people say,
So listen up, And I just may, First things to remember,
Im boss of my brain, My choices are all mine,
And thats always the same,
Next comes the breathing, You must do it
right, Breathe from the belly, And take air inside,
Now five second lightswitch, Is a really
great tool, You take a bad thought, And you do
something cool,
Positive is next, You times it by three,
Thoughts, Words, and actions, You choose what
will be, Is it positive, Is it powerfull, Will
it produce something sweet, If you answered
no, Then you must work on these.
Next you must claim, Responsibility
and such, Its not about the past, But the future
of much, You claim what just happened, And
disgaurd the crutch,
Now you let go, And I know that
this sounds hard, Just drop past misdeeds,
Redefine who you are,
Forgive happens next, This is number
nine, Just make sure your safe, Erase bad
from your mind, Use new for the giving,
And happiness you'll find,

Now what if is next, It is number ten, Your thinking about your future, When reality check sets in, You have come so far, From where you first did start, Reflect on your progress, And take it to the heart.

Last but not least, Big number twelve, Ultimate freedom, Will help good prevail.

These are the tools, That gogi provides, With power so great, All goodness will thrive, I'm so glad you listened, To what I just said, Now go and spread the word, So gogi can live!

By John P
Stickney

John
Awesome!!
So very GOGI
You can be leader
for Good forever!!
Coach

THIS IS ANOTHER IN THE FAMILY OF GOGI BOOKS

Published by: Getting Out By Going In (GOGI)
PO Box 88969 – Los Angeles, CA, USA 90009
www.gettingoutbygoingin.org

Getting Out By Going In (GOGI) is a non-profit organization. Profits from this book go directly to providing GOGI materials to indigent men, women and children in prisons and jails.

ISBN: 0-9882908-6-3

Typesetting and layout by Candace Webster.
Editing by Joan Ashley.
GOGI Icon artwork by Loren Barnhart.
Contributions by GOGI students, Coaches, and community members.

This book is another in the family of GOGI materials such as: workshops, curricula, educational media and self-study materials designed to teach the GOGI TOOLS for POSITIVE DECISION MAKING.

YOUR LIFE CAN BE BETTER WITH GOGI

You probably know your life can be better. It is likely that you have wanted to make your life better for a while now, but many things you have tried have not lasted long.

If that is your experience, the information in this book might be what is missing in your efforts to make lasting changes. Even if your life is pretty good, what you will learn in this book may help you make it even better.

WHAT IS GOGI?

Getting Out By Going In (GOGI) helps you "get out" of negative situations by "going in" to your own ability to find the solutions.

By "getting out" we mean freeing you from negative thoughts, actions and reactions. By "going in" we mean providing you with simple tools for you to change your life starting with changes inside you. "GOGI" is the nickname. It sounds like yogi.

GOGI-ism

A GOGI-ism is a catchy phrase created by a student of GOGI to help them incorporate the GOGI Tools into their everyday choices. You may wish to create your OWN GOGI-isms to help you use your GOGI TOOLS!

GOGI was developed by people who were suffering and struggling to find freedom from addictions, poor decisions, negative associations, and terrible actions. GOGI was developed from the heart and soul of this struggle, and is now available and given to you to aid you in your journey to freedom. This is a gift to you, a gift from the voices of those who have remained silent for too long.

♡ Coach

GOGI-ism

Getting Out by Going In (GOGI)

In 2002, when it was nothing more than a group of prisoners joining together for a "relaxation class" held in a prison chapel each week, Coach Taylor shared with the men that freedom was actually "within" each of them. One man chimed in, "getting out of prison by going in for the answers?" And that is how Getting Out by Going In got its name.

Contents

Welcome to GOGI

My name is Coach Mara L. Taylor and in 2002 I sat down and began to listen to men and women and children who were put in prisons and jails because of their addictions and poor decision making. I listened to tens of thousands of prisoners for more than 10 years and during that time, I witnessed their struggle, hopelessness, despair, regret, remorse, sorrow, guilt and sadness.

Coach Mara L. Taylor
GOGI Founder/lead volunteer

Through this process of active listening, the prisoners taught me many things including how to find my own internal freedom. Thousands of prisoners helped me to formulate the tools you are going to learn in this book.

Each tool was designed by prisoners and only added to the GOGI 'toolbox' after being tested and circulated to thousands of prisoners asking for their comments and opinions.

If these tools work for individuals who have made the most poor decisions possible, I have a feeling they might work for you, too. As Herbert Smith, a prisoner in Utah stated, "If I can be GOGI, then anyone can be GOGI." Like many people, Herbert has had a lifetime of poor decision making. But, now he studies - AND TEACHES - GOGI each week to fellow prisoners, and his life is changing each and every day for the better.

Can GOGI work for you? I promise you this, if you keep this book handy and you read just one page each day for the rest of your life, I believe your life will turn out better than you could ever have imagined.

I have seen change happen with thousands and thousands of individuals who have suffered for too long and reach for GOGI as a possible solution. They use their tools and life gets better.

Welcome to GOGI. Welcome to a growing family of happy people. Smile. You are about to learn how to find a rare form of freedom with GOGI.

Love,

Coach

Coach Mara L. Taylor
Lead volunteer

The First GOGI Family

Coach David Merrihue, Coach Maria Fierro and GOGI Girl Diamond Merrihue

Coach Maria Fierro celebrates earning her college degree with her husband, Coach David Merrihue, and their daughter, Diamond, by her side.

I am 9 years old and I am GOGI GIRL Diamond and GOGI to me is my family because we have fun and laugh a lot. we draw pictures and write letters to our bigger family who needs encouragement. GOGI went and taught BOSS OF MY BRAIN to my whole school and that is one of my best memories so far! Me my Dad and Mom are the 1st GOGI family!

YOUR GOGI COACHES

While GOGI listens to prisoners and all GOGI materials are the "voice of the prisoner" it took a team of physically free people to make this book happen. Below are the four individuals who have poured their heart and soul into the growth of GOGI and who are now so very proud to include their contributions to this GOGI Book:

Coach Mara L. Taylor

Coach Taylor was the first volunteer who had a hunch that the prisoners knew a lot more about how to solve the prison problem than they might have been given credit for. That was in 2002, when she first began listening to the prisoners who she credits with giving her the internal freedom she now enjoys. She pulled together all the pieces that went into this book you now hold.

Coach Carlson has the second longest record for volunteerism to GOGI, second only to the founder, Coach Taylor. While maintaining full time employment, Coach Carlson also logs no less than 30-40 hours each week as GOGI's top volunteer. She was promoted to the position of National Director of Programs and Media for which she is paid --- nothing. Throughout this book, she explains in detail each of the tools to give you greater insight.

Coach Leigh Carlson

Coach David and **Coach Fierro** have their hands full with full time employment and raising a daughter, but it does not stop them from expanding GOGI into communities and supporting any volunteer who wishes to earn their certified facilitator status or attend one of our community groups. They have written the foreword to this book and are fundraising to support our ability to offer the book at the lowest cost to facilities and organizations.

Coach David Merrihue
Coach Maria Fierro

FOREWORD

Coach Merrihue

Coach David Merrihue

If you happen to pick up a GOGI book and you see the cover, you won't automatically know what is in it that might help you change your life. But, you have opened the book. That means you are closer to success than if you had just let this book pass you by.

When I first received a GOGI book it was back in 2008. To be honest and real with you, I put the book down and thought the book was hogwash before even reading a word. I didn't think my life could change and certainly didn't think the answer was in a book sent to me while I was a prisoner at Pelican Bay State Prison in California. But, for some unknown reason, I picked the book up after tossing it aside. I picked it up not once, not twice, but three different times and I finally sat down and started going through it page by page.

The first thing that came to my mind was reading that prisoners developed the GOGI Tools for Positive Decision Making. That caught my attention and I kept reading.

So here I am in 2015. Incredible. I am now living a life I never thought was possible for an addict and criminal like me. And the thing is that I am the perfect person to help addicts and criminals! In me, they can see what is possible with GOGI.

Who would have thought that by me picking up a GOGI book, that I could learn the tools needed to create the life I have today? Who would have thought by me picking up that GOGI book that I would be clean and sober now for 7 years? Who would have thought that by me picking up a GOGI book that I would be going back to jails and prisons to help men and women who I have never met before as they begin their GOGI journey?

Who would have thought I would be a case manager, an active father, a solid husband, a good friend, and a GOGI volunteer?

I am a PLUS to society, and not a minus today. I earn a paycheck. I pay taxes. I pay my bills and put a roof over my family's head. I used to shy away and hated to talk to authority, correctional officers, probation officers, parole agents and most of all, the LA County Sheriffs cuz they would slap cuffs on me for just about anything.

Now, I rub shoulders with everyone, even the badge wearing people. Truthfully, everyone needs GOGI and I will share GOGI with anyone who wants to create a better life.

For those of you who have doubts about this book, all I can say is if you knew me in 2008 there is no way you would say I am the same person. Since the age of 13 I was in trouble, doing 16.5 years inside prisons and jails before becoming GOGI. I was doing life on the installment plan.

I know, beyond any doubt whatsoever, that you CAN change. I am proof. Who knows? Maybe it is your turn? You DID pick up this book. Maybe you are like me and all you need are the GOGI TOOLS FOR POSITIVE DECISION MAKING to help you pull all your experience, your learning, your successes and failures together to create a life you never thought possible.

GOGI Por Vida,

Coach Merrihue

Coach Merrihue

(Coach Merrihue's motivation)

Coach Fierro

Coach Maria Fierro

Wow. I can't believe that you are actually going to be reading the words on this page that are coming directly from my heart. It seems as if every day there is another miracle showing up in my life. You reading this is just one more miracle for me.

You see, it's only been six years since I first got introduced to GOGI. I was living away from my husband and my daughter as an inmate at the Los Angeles County Jail. Luckily, I made the choice to be housed in a housing unit called GOGI Campus, where other mothers, sisters and daughters were housed.

It wasn't that long ago, really, but it seems so far away because of how much my life has changed since the day I wore county blues and was called by my inmate number. I have moved forward so firmly and steadily because I became committed to implementing the GOGI TOOLS into every aspect of my life. It seems as if the more I put the tools into practice, the more great things happen in my life and in the lives of my husband and daughter.

It is true that you only keep those things you are willing to give away. Now that I give freely of my time to anyone who wants to learn GOGI, it seems as if I am able to keep my internal freedom. And, because I am willing to be of service, I now share what I have learned with an increasing number of people who are joining the GOGI family. I go into jails, prisons, transition homes, community groups, even to schools to teach children the GOGI TOOLS FOR POSITIVE DECISION MAKING.

These simple tools were not taught to me as a child. My mother was in prison when she gave birth to me. I was born in prison. But now I have GOGI and I am grateful and thankful that the tools are simple enough that my daughter now lives her life guided by the GOGI TOOLS. The GOGI TOOLS work. I always say I thank God for GOGI.

You may be reading this thinking to yourself "OK, that is her story, but what about mine?" Here is what I know. You are reading this book. The mere fact that you have picked this book up and are reading these words means you have something within you that knows the truth of your purpose, the truth of what you are capable of contributing if you have the right tools. My suggestion? Take advantage of the fact that you have this book in your hands right now. While you may not believe it to be so, you may be more ready than you believe to make lasting changes in your life. As you begin to read this book and do the work on your own or in a GOGI Group, you may be questioning BOSS OF MY BRAIN, BELLY BREATHING, or the other names of the tools. Believe me, the tools work. They were designed by prisoners who practiced them, tested them and began to live THE GOGI WAY. Now they are sharing their successes with you.

We need you. We need you as part of the growing GOGI family. We need exactly who you are, where you have been, what you have done and all that has been done to you. We need your experience. And we need you to make a stand for the change GOGI knows is possible. We need your support and your individuality in workshops teaching others. We need your support and your individuality that only you can offer to others as proof that change is possible. We need you in the schools, in the jails, in the prisons, in the communities, in the programs, in the GOGI mailrooms. And, basically, the world needs you to show them that you, too, can put the GOGI TOOLS to work in your life.

I am in a place today that I can honestly, genuinely, and sincerely tell you, that I can do it and that you can do it and that together we are unstoppable. With all my progress in life and recovery from addiction, my life is full. One day, I hope to receive forgiveness from my older children, who I have always loved. Once I decided to put the tools to work, believe in myself, others, and to believe that I was worthy and I deserved to give myself a chance, that is when the GOGI way of life took off for me. It will do the same for you. That is my promise.

Unshakable Faith,

Coach Fierro

Coach Fierro

Meet the First GOGI Family Introduction by Coach Taylor

When Coach Fierro was once inmate Maria, she asked if I could find a donor to pay for her husband to have a GOGI book. She was in the county jail and he was at Pelican Bay state prison in Northern California. They were both doing time, again, for crimes related to drug use and sales. In the wake of their lifestyle, their daughter, Diamond, was left without a mother or father to tuck her into bed each night. Fighting to regain custody of her child became Coach Fierro's motivation and she embraced the GOGI TOOLS FOR POSITIVE DECISION MAKING as a crucial key to uniting her family once and for all.

Over a two-year period, starting when she was an inmate, Coach Fierro completed the 2-year requirement and study and became certified as a GOGI Coach. Her husband, Coach Merrihue, too, eventually earned his certification as a GOGI Coach.

They have become GOGI's first GOGI Family. At their home they speak GOGI and the tools are integrated into the fabric of their life. Their hobbies are related to the GOGI mailroom, GOGI outings, GOGI workshops and

GOGI service projects. Coach Fierro became an ordained interfaith minister so she could work better with prisoners and others learning their GOGI Tools from a spiritual or religious perspective. Coach Merrihue will complete his ordination as an interfaith minister next year. Diamond sings GOGI songs and will tell you how her parents use their GOGI Tools to make each day better.

By fusing their family together with GOGI, Coach Fierro and Coach Merrihue have locked in their position as a forever-sober family. They are a law-abiding family. They are a 'big plus' to society.

What is remarkable is the fact that any human can use GOGI like Coach Merrihue and Coach Fierro. Families can be families for good when the family is focused on using the GOGI TOOLS FOR POSITIVE DECISION MAKING.

And, I can promise you this, your life will not ever be worse off with GOGI. Your life will only get better. And better. And better. For as long as you are dedicated to making positive decisions, your life will get better. It may not be immediate. It may not be drastic at first. But, over time you will find that you have incrementally created a life you never, ever thought possible.

When in doubt, just think of Coach Fierro sitting in a cell wondering how on earth she was going to repair the damage in her life. You can do that, too.

♡ Coach

WHY DO I HAVE THIS BOOK?

GOGI has many different types of books to help different types of people who wish to make more positive decisions in their lives. This book, TEACH ME HOW TO GOGI, was inspired by GOGI students who were returning to their communities and wanted to continue their GOGI studies, share GOGI and make a positive difference in their community. They wanted a book that could guide people in community with and without the experience of incarceration toward a better life with the application of the GOGI TOOLS FOR POSITIVE DECISION MAKING.

The first GOGI graduates offered to teach a GOGI Group at adult probation and parole. Another taught GOGI at a reentry home and a resource center for the homeless. Eventually GOGI materials were used by parents returning home and teaching their children the GOGI Tools. This book is an ideal guide for all GOGI groups, and is a great support for individuals that are taking GOGI to the streets.

IN PRISON? If you are incarcerated, this book is in your hands so you can strengthen your knowledge of your GOGI Tools, have an excellent group guide, and begin to prepare yourself to return to your community as a GOGI Volunteer. It is those individuals with the experience in rising up from the ashes of a burned-out life that cause others to listen with an open heart. Even individuals who do not know if they are going home can begin to re-think their situation once they begin to master the use and teaching of the GOGI Tools as a humble volunteer dedicated to helping others.

WORKER IN PRISON? If your job is working with the incarcerated, this book is an ideal tool to help expand the use of positive decision-making tools within your population. If you permit your clients/students/caseload to hold, have, and take ownership of GOGI, they will surprise you with their determination and commitment to making positive decisions.

FAMILY OR FRIEND? If you are a family member or friend of an incarcerated GOGI student, you will find this book will make it very easy for your relationship to be based on powerful, productive and positive interactions and activities. When two or more people are united in service, their relationship strengthens.

NO CONNECTION? If you have no connection to prisoners and have just picked up this book, know that this book is good for all men and women, because, in a very real way, we are each in a prison of our own making until we begin to live our life in service of those around us. Maybe now is the time for you to break free through service to others.

Why do you have this book? Let's see what you think after you learn what this book has to offer to your life.

ACKNOWLEDGEMENTS

Facilities and organizations that purchase GOGI learning materials are increasing in numbers. They are finding that people are more likely to change in positive ways when provided with the simple tools GOGI offers. We acknowledge these facilities and their sincere support for making our communities safer by supporting GOGI studies.

We also acknowledge our volunteers and our donors who help us make Getting Out by Going In (GOGI) available to men, women and children who are ready for lasting change. We especially appreciate our growing number of students, peer facilitators and coaches who are living proof that change can happen and that living life THE GOGI WAY is an easy way to create a better life.

INTRODUCTION

This book is a powerful companion for any GOGI Group study or GOGI self-study. The group or class setting may be as small as two people holding a meeting, or it can be a more formal GOGI Group, or even part of a program. For self-study, this book provides all of the information needed to learn the GOGI TOOLS and apply them in your daily life. For group study, each tool is presented in a way that will engage and involve the group members and facilitators.

WHY SHOULD YOU USE THIS BOOK?

Do You Feel Trapped or Stuck?

If you have ever felt as if life happened to you rather than you being in charge of your life, then you are really going to enjoy what you will learn and practice in this book. That is because with the tools in this book, you will learn how to take charge of your life.

You Are in Charge

This book will help you learn to make more positive decisions. This is very important because:

- When you make more positive decisions, you will find that you are in charge.
- When you are in charge, you will realize that you can manage even the most difficult situations.
- When you can manage difficult situations better, there is less stress and anxiety, and daily tasks seem easier.
- When you understand that you are in charge of your future, that it is in your control and that you can use the tools to make your life better from this day forward, you have a powerful, productive and positive sense of self-control.

All this is possible when you use the tools you will learn in this book.

You Can Create a Better Life

Using the GOGI TOOLS may help you experience many new things. Below is a short list of what GOGI students say they experience when they become the boss of their life and start using the tools each day:

- With GOGI you may find you are more peaceful each day.
- With GOGI you may find you are more relaxed and focused.
- With GOGI you may find your relationships are easier.
- With GOGI you may find you do not get bothered or upset as easily.
- With GOGI you may find you are healthier and happier.
- With GOGI you may find overcoming addiction is easier.
- With GOGI you may find that you are better at your program or school.
- With GOGI you may find you are more comfortable where you live.
- With GOGI you may find you are more likely to get and keep a job.

GOGI-ism

The Acronym GOGI

When the first group of prisoners heard the phrase "getting out by going in" one of the guys made a joke and said, "Yeah, GOGI. Getting Out by Going In." And that is how GOGI came to be the common name for Getting Out by Going In. Remember, this first prisoner said GOGI with a hard G, so it rhymes with Yogi. Like Yogi Bear, GOGI has two hard G sounds. Go-Ghee.

GOGI BASICS

GOGI Tools — All Twelve Tools

There are twelve GOGI TOOLS FOR POSITIVE DECISION MAKING and these tools work best when they are learned and practiced one tool each week.

The GOGI TOOLS:

TOOLS OF THE BODY

BOSS OF MY BRAIN

BELLY BREATHING

FIVE SECOND LIGHTSWITCH

TOOLS OF CHOICE

POSITIVE THOUGHTS

POSITIVE WORDS

POSITIVE ACTIONS

TOOLS OF MOVING FORWARD

CLAIM RESPONSIBILITY

LET GO

FOR--GIVE

TOOLS OF CREATION

WHAT IF

REALITY CHECK

ULTIMATE FREEDOM

The Four Sections

Each tool belongs to a section of tools. There are four sections:

TOOLS OF THE BODY

TOOLS OF CHOICE

TOOLS OF MOVING FORWARD

TOOLS OF CREATION

Each Section Has Three Tools

Each section of the GOGI TOOLS and each section of this book is made up of three tools. When you have learned the three tools in a section it means you have completed one full section of GOGI. When you complete all four sections over a twelve week period, you will have learned all of the GOGI TOOLS FOR POSITIVE DECISION MAKING.

I THANK YOU FOR MAKING THIS CURRICULUM AVAILABLE TO THOSE THAT ARE SEEKING AN OPPORTUNITY TO CHANGE THEIR LIVES AND BECOME BETTER HUMAN BEINGS. AS A RESULT OF APPLYING THE GOGI TOOLS TO MY LIFE, I AM "BOSS OF MY BRAIN". I DO THIS BY UTILIZING "FIVE SECOND LIGHTSWITCH", FOLLOWED BY "BELLY BREATHING". THIS PROCESS IS FOLLOWED BY WHAT I CALL THE POSITIVE THREE, "POSITIVE THOUGHTS", "POSITIVE WORDS", AND "POSITIVE ACTIONS". THIS IS HOW I UTILIZE SOME OF THE GOGI TOOLS IN MY LIFE.

– ANTHONY W.

Completion of Sections

Even if you only complete one section, this can be really powerful in your life. It means you have three tools for positive decision making that you can use any time, any day, and any way you like.

Your Success

You will be a successful student of GOGI when you do the following:

- ☐ Follow The **National Calendar.**
- ☐ **Study** only one tool each week so you can learn to apply the tool for the entire week.
- ☐ Follow the **Meeting Format** with one or more people for maximum study effectiveness.
- ☐ Become active in **group study** of the tools.
- ☐ **Practice** the tools every day, each week.
- ☐ **Share** the tool each week with someone.

Many people tend to judge and give up on those who have made bad choices in their lives. Some of us were never taught how to live a positive life. This book is able to give us some tools to make wise choices and live a productive life as citizens in society. It also gives us the ability to pass down our own growth and knowledge to those who are still trying to find their way.

- Tony U.

Take Back Your Power

By Gregory G.

Living in this world with ups and downs
Learning how to be the BOSS OF MY BRAIN
When all I want to do is maintain.

Now I am really feeling the flow
BELLY BREATHING steady as I go
In an environment filled with hate and discontent,
using my FIVE SECOND LIGHTSWITCH.
Even though all I know
Is heartache and pain
I still try to keep POSITIVE THOUGHTS
running around my brain.

Making it easier for POSITIVE WORDS
to come to my mouth
Now good deeds and POSITIVE ACTIONS
is what I'm about!
Now I'm turned out and through new eyes
I see CLAIM RESPONSIBILITY.

No more waiting for tomorrow, because I own today
So live and LET GO with open arms to FOR – GIVE.
Is it safe? So I ask the question WHAT IF?
Although I know it's always darkest before the light
The REALITY CHECK is no longer hindsight.

Focus and ULTIMATE FREEDOM you will receive
Remember it's always been in your hands
Now from this day forward, all limitations end!

THE GOGI Calendar

Across the nation, no matter where you are, when you study according to the GOGI Calendar, you will never be alone in your GOGI studies. It is MORE IMPORTANT to be on the Calendar than to start GOGI studies with a particular tool.

Why Study According to the Calendar?

GOGI is studied by thousands upon thousands of students in every state of the United States and even in foreign countries. You are not alone, nor will you ever be alone with GOGI. There are GOGI students nearly everywhere using their tools to make better decisions. Then, when they are strong enough, they begin to teach the GOGI TOOLS to their children, family, and friends. Our GOGI Calendar lets all GOGI students study the same tool at the same time, regardless of where they live.

As a successful GOGI student, you will follow the GOGI Calendar of study. If your group is not following the GOGI Calendar, bring this up to the group facilitator. Tell the group leader that you want to be in the best possible GOGI group and you suggest your group follow the schedule of other groups.

As you progress and continue your GOGI studies, and after your class or course is complete, you can remain connected to GOGI by focusing on the GOGI Calendar and the GOGI TOOLS being studied by others.

The Order of Things

It may help you feel supported to know that you are practicing the same GOGI tool being studied all over the world. It is most important that you study the tools as they are listed on the GOGI Calendar so that every GOGI group you come across will feel like home to you, because they will be studying the same GOGI tool.

Or, if you are alone and studying your GOGI TOOLS, it may help to know that you are not really alone. All of GOGI studies the same tool on the same week; our students are like one big GOGI family, all focused on learning a specific tool each week. Since GOGI TOOLS are not "steps" you do not need to start on the first tool.

Start in the Middle

Some groups begin their GOGI studies in the middle of the tools, because that is what is represented in the calendar. That is fine. As long as the group is on the GOGI Calendar, you will know that your group has joined others practicing that same tool.

When you study this way, you will be able to discover which tool works best for you. Remember, you only need one tool to make lasting changes in your life, but because you want the most success, you will learn the other tools, so you always have a back up.

When to Start GOGI

If you want to begin your GOGI studies with BOSS OF MY BRAIN, which is the first tool listed in the GOGI books, then you can study with other GOGI students who are on the GOGI calendar by starting your study on:

January	First week	BOSS OF MY BRAIN
April	First week	BOSS OF MY BRAIN
July	First week	BOSS OF MY BRAIN
October	First week	BOSS OF MY BRAIN

If your group begins with BOSS OF MY BRAIN on those weeks, you will be studying the same tool studied by other official GOGI Groups.

Don't Wait

You do not need to wait to start GOGI. Start GOGI in the middle of the book if that is what the Calendar states. That is OK. When you follow the GOGI National Calendar, you are part of a huge GOGI family.

The three tools of the body are: BOSS OF MY BRAIN, BELLY BREATHING, and FIVE SECOND LIGHTSWITCH. These tools help us focus on the smart part of our brain, make positive decision while maintaining our composure, and have new actions ready when we encounter old thoughts. I apply BOSS OF MY BRAIN by asking myself which part of my brain am I using during emotional moments or when old thoughts come to mind. BELLY BREATHING is applied when I find myself tensed up and I'm breathing from my chest. FIVE SECOND LIGHTSWITCH has given me a new action to have on stand-by when I find myself ruminating on an old thought and counterattack my impulsiveness. *– Lawrence E.*

THE GOGI Calendar

***Whenever there is a fifth Monday in the month, review all four tools.**

JANUARY

Week 1 BOSS OF MY BRAIN
Week 2 BELLY BREATHING
Week 3 FIVE SECOND LIGHTSWITCH
Week 4 POSITIVE THOUGHTS

FEBRUARY

Week 1 POSITIVE WORDS
Week 2 POSITIVE ACTIONS
Week 3 CLAIM RESPONSIBILITY
Week 4 LET GO

MARCH

Week 1 FOR--GIVE
Week 2 WHAT IF
Week 3 REALITY CHECK
Week 4 ULTIMATE FREEDOM

APRIL

Week 1 BOSS OF MY BRAIN
Week 2 BELLY BREATHING
Week 3 FIVE SECOND LIGHTSWITCH
Week 4 POSITIVE THOUGHTS

MAY

Week 1 POSITIVE WORDS
Week 2 POSITIVE ACTIONS
Week 3 CLAIM RESPONSIBILITY
Week 4 LET GO

JUNE

Week 1 FOR--GIVE
Week 2 WHAT IF
Week 3 REALITY CHECK
Week 4 ULTIMATE FREEDOM

THE GOGI Calendar

***Whenever there is a fifth Monday in the month, review all four tools.**

JULY

Week 1 BOSS OF MY BRAIN
Week 2 BELLY BREATHING
Week 3 FIVE SECOND LIGHTSWITCH
Week 4 POSITIVE THOUGHTS

AUGUST

Week 1 POSITIVE WORDS
Week 2 POSITIVE ACTIONS
Week 3 CLAIM RESPONSIBILITY
Week 4 LET GO

SEPTEMBER

Week 1 FOR--GIVE
Week 2 WHAT IF
Week 3 REALITY CHECK
Week 4 ULTIMATE FREEDOM

OCTOBER

Week 1 BOSS OF MY BRAIN
Week 2 BELLY BREATHING
Week 3 FIVE SECOND LIGHTSWITCH
Week 4 POSITIVE THOUGHTS

NOVEMBER

Week 1 POSITIVE WORDS
Week 2 POSITIVE ACTIONS
Week 3 CLAIM RESPONSIBILITY
Week 4 LET GO

DECEMBER

Week 1 FOR--GIVE
Week 2 WHAT IF
Week 3 REALITY CHECK
Week 4 ULTIMATE FREEDOM

" I would like to shar a personal story with everyone. I have really put my heart & soul into working the GOGI program since I learned of it. Really working the tools in my everyday life. Well I received a email from my dad a Couple weeks ago and at the end he says; "Son, you sure do have a real Positive Attitude these days". The thing is that he has not been able to say that to me since I was about 13 yrs old. I am 39 now. When I read it I cryed right there at the Computer. My attitude was so bad and I was so full of anger and hate for so long I never gave him the Chance to say them words. Thank you GOGI family.

Pacheco and I are going to take a picture real soon to send yall.

Keep your head up and stay strong.

Respectfully,

Ronald

THE OFFICIAL GOGI Meeting Format

If you are learning GOGI in a group or with another person and you want maximum success, you will use your GOGI Meeting Format. Remember, a GOGI group can be held with just two people, or a GOGI Group can be a larger, more official meeting.

The ideal size of a GOGI group is 8 to 10 people. We have seen rooms with 100 GOGI students who open the meeting, then break into a small group for GOGI learning. Even if you are studying GOGI on your own, the Meeting Format is a good guide for you. Large groups are best when broken down into smaller groups for their meetings.

The best and most effective GOGI Groups follow the GOGI Meeting Format. This is to provide reinforcement of the tools, increase community harmony, and strengthen your familiarity with applying the GOGI TOOLS to your daily life.

GOGI-ism

GOGI Por Vida

When Spanish-speaking GOGI students began translating GOGI material into their native language, it was natural for them to claim "GOGI POR VIDA" as their own.

Example of Your GOGI Meeting Format as Suggested in Each Chapter

Call Your Meeting to Order

(Volunteer to open the meeting) *"We call this meeting to order. The purpose of GOGI is to provide simple tools to anyone interested in making more positive decisions in their lives."*

Reading of Your Tools

(Volunteer to read)

The GOGI TOOLS FOR POSITIVE DECISION MAKING are:

BOSS OF MY BRAIN
BELLY BREATHING
FIVE SECOND LIGHTSWITCH
POSITIVE THOUGHTS
POSITIVE WORDS
POSITIVE ACTIONS
CLAIM RESPONSIBILITY
LET GO
FOR--GIVE
WHAT IF
REALITY CHECK
ULTIMATE FREEDOM

Check-in/Recap of Your Prior Week

A brief check-in on last week's tool.

Your GOGI National Calendar

(Volunteer to state the tool of the week as found in the national Calendar) *"According to the National Calendar, students of GOGI are studying the tool of (see Calendar) this week."*

Your Reading

Volunteers to take turns reading the information about the tool of the week from this book.

Your Activity

In pairs or small groups each activity is completed.

Your Group Questions

The questions at the end of the chapter are discussed.

GOGI Pledge

(Volunteer to read) Please repeat after me:

May our commitment (repeat)
To the study of GOGI (repeat)
Grant us the joy (repeat)
Of giving and receiving (repeat)
So that our inner freedom (repeat)
May be of maximum service (repeat)
To those we love (repeat)
And infinite others (repeat)

Close Your Meeting

(Volunteer to Close Your Meeting)
We invite you to join us for our next meeting to be held (date) where we will study the GOGI Tool (refer to Calendar).

Xavier H.

SECTION ONE:

Teach Me How to GOGI

TOOLS OF THE BODY

BOSS OF MY BRAIN

BELLY BREATHING

FIVE SECOND LIGHTSWITCH

BOSS OF MY BRAIN

I am BOSS OF MY BRAIN and I have complete control over each thought I create. Because I am BOSS OF MY BRAIN, I can change my thoughts at any time. No one has control over my thoughts because only I am the BOSS OF MY BRAIN.

Repeat this week's statement of ownership as often as possible. Before you get out of bed, before your meals, during a break, and before sleeping. Write this statement for added emphasis. Your weekly statement of ownership reinforces this week's tool.

MY GOGI TOOL

BOSS OF MY BRAIN

Weeks to study

BOSS OF MY BRAIN are:

1st Week of January

1st Week of April

1st Week of July

1st Week of October

KEY WORDS

BOSS OF MY BRAIN

THE THREE PARTS

There are three parts that matter: SMART PART, EMOTIONAL PART and the OLD HABIT PART. Which one is the boss right now?

GOGI - JANUARY

S M T W T F S

BOSS OF MY BRAIN

2nd week of the month

3rd week of the month

4th week of the month

GOGI - APRIL

S M T W T F S

BOSS OF MY BRAIN

2nd week of the month

3rd week of the month

4th week of the month

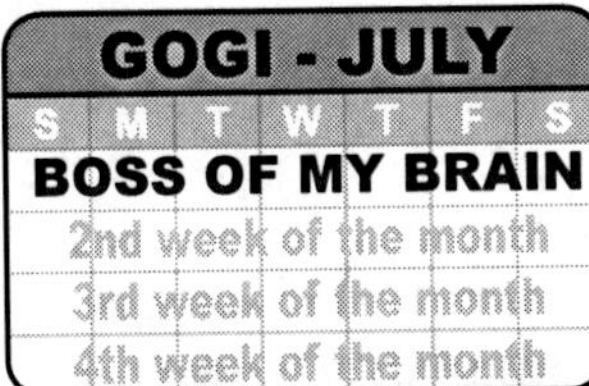

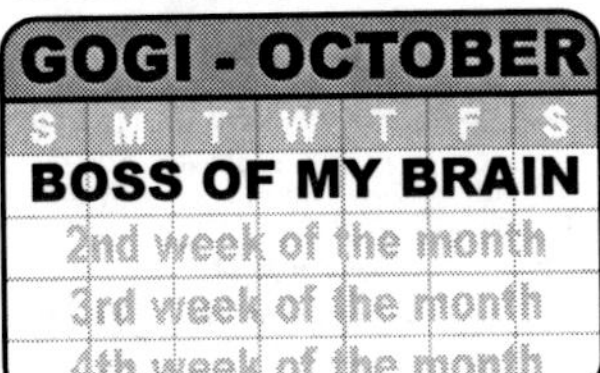

OBJECTIVE – BOSS OF MY BRAIN

Your goal with this week's tool is to learn that you have a choice in how your brain thinks.

You can SMART think, EMOTIONAL think, or you can OLD HABIT think. You are the boss of how you think and you will learn how to be the boss with this week's tool called BOSS OF MY BRAIN.

GOGI-ism

GOGI Coach

When the first group of prisoners sat in their weekly group at a Federal prison, one of the men asked of the facilitator, "What are you? Are you a teacher? Preacher? Psychologist?" When none of those titles fit, Coach Taylor responded, "I am just a community volunteer who thinks you can make more positive choices in your life." One of the prisoners said, "kinda like a Coach?" And that is how the title of Coach was given to Coach Taylor and all the men and women who earn certification as a GOGI Coach.

AGENDA – BOSS OF MY BRAIN

Here is the outline for this week's 90-minute GOGI class/group:

1. Call Your Meeting to Order (1 min)
2. Reading of your GOGI Tools (1 min)
3. Check-in/Recap of Last Week
   A very short recap (10 mins)
4. Check GOGI national calendar
   What is the tool of this week? (1 min)
5. Reading and Activity
   For this tool from this chapter (30 mins)
6. Group Discussions
   Found in this chapter (40-50 mins)
7. Closing Thoughts (1 min)
8. Your GOGI Pledge & Close of Meeting (2-5 mins)

GOGI-ism

To be "GOGI'd"

R. Petersen is known for spreading GOGI in her work with students in a drug treatment program. When one of her students was asked how he became involved with GOGI, he said "Ms. Petersen GOGI'd me and I didn't even know it."

TOOL INTRO – BOSS OF MY BRAIN

Did you know that GOGI believes there are only three parts of your brain you need to understand? At GOGI we focus on three parts of your brain:

THE THREE PARTS

- The SMART part
- The EMOTIONAL part
- The OLD HABIT part

The Ultimate Mind Tune up.

Old Habits
Emotional
Smart Part

Art by Gordon K.

HOW TO USE – BOSS OF MY BRAIN

If you want to use the GOGI TOOL called BOSS OF MY BRAIN, all you need to do is ask yourself, "What part of my brain is in charge right now?" It's that simple.

- The **SMART PART** of your brain is where you learn new things. This is the part of the brain that will help you be strong and make positive decisions.
- The **EMOTIONAL PART** is filled with opinions, drama, anger, or hurt. When you let this part of your brain be the boss, you are not going to make positive decisions.
- The **OLD HABIT PART** of your brain is where all those old habits you no longer need are stored. The less you rely on old habits, the more room you will have for the **SMART PART** to help you create new positive habits.

Whatever I put into my Brain (my computer) its of my own doing, unless I give in to let Someone be the Boss of my Brain. I have a smart part, Emotional Part, old habit part. Knowing these three components of my brain really helped me identify and understand me and my brain. Thought processes can be like a bad virus when negative, impulsive old behavior patterns try to creep back in and take over. Its imperative that I not fall back into my old thought system of thinking, saying, and actions and reactions when dealing with lifes obstacles and struggles and challenges. Smart Part works

Frank M.

ACTIVITY – BOSS OF MY BRAIN

Alone, with another person, or in small groups, you can enjoy this activity.

1. FOREHEAD – Please touch your forehead. Right behind your forehead is the SMART PART of your brain. Give an example to your partner or group of when you make smart decisions and when you are using SMART PART thinking.

2. EARS – Now touch your ears. Between your two ears, in the middle of your head, is the EMOTIONAL PART of your brain. Give an example to your partner or group of when you make emotional decisions and are letting the EMOTIONAL PART be the boss.

3. BACK OF HEAD – Now put your hand on the back of your head. That is where the OLD HABIT THINKING happens. Give an example of some OLD HABIT THINKING, which has controlled you in the past.

REVIEW – After everyone in your group has completed this activity you can have each member touch their forehead and state one thing they will do every day this week which is using the SMART PART for SMART THINKING."

REVIEW – BOSS OF MY BRAIN

All you do is ask, "What part of my brain is working right now? Am I using my SMART part, EMOTIONAL part or OLD HABIT part?"

If you ask yourself this question, then you are using the GOGI tool BOSS OF MY BRAIN. If you use no other tool, BOSS OF MY BRAIN is enough for you to be the boss of your life and make the changes that will allow you to enjoy each day a little more.

Some GOGI students find it easy to be the BOSS when they touch their forehead to remind themselves to be SMART THINKING.

When You relize that you are the boss of your brain You have the power to change the world around you!

David C.

From Coach Taylor
BOSS OF MY BRAIN

When I was explaining how the brain worked to a group of prisoners, one guy spoke up and said, "What you are telling us, Coach, is that I can be the BOSS OF MY BRAIN." That was how this tool got its name.

Every one of the GOGI TOOLS was developed by men and women who had struggled many years and had made decisions which hurt them and others. In listening to them, it was easy to see they wanted to make the choices leading to a positive life, they just didn't have the tools. In developing the tools, they discovered they could change and make that change last.

After more than a decade of working with men and women and children in prisons or trapped inside a prison of their own mind, I have come to realize that the GOGI TOOL, BOSS OF MY BRAIN can unlock even the most stubborn of prison doors. When all of life's events are filtered though this tool, any individual (and I do mean any individual) has the power to control and direct their reactions and responses. Life might not be fair, but BOSS OF MY BRAIN sure puts you in the driver's seat.

♡ Coach

Thoughts from Coach Leigh Carlson

Coach Carlson

Coach Carlson was appointed as GOGI's National Director of Programs and Media in 2013 after four years of nearly full-time volunteerism for GOGI. In her current volunteer position, she is responsible for coordinating with institutions of corrections as they implement GOGI into their programming. In each chapter, she will provide insights and her perspective into maximizing the GOGI TOOLS FOR POSITIVE DECISION MAKING.

I am BOSS MY BRAIN. Say that to yourself. I am BOSS OF MY BRAIN. A powerful realization for me in my life was how I relate to my brain and how I choose to process thoughts and information is 100% up to me. When I first realized that I am the BOSS OF MY BRAIN, it immediately gave me a positive sense of self-control and confidence I had been lacking my entire life. I always thought others made me think, feel, speak and act a certain way. "They made me do it." "They made me feel this way." No one made me feel or do anything. I am in control. I can choose to think a specific thought or feel a certain way, regardless of others opinions or actions. This simple, yet powerful fact propelled me into a life where my decisions are filtered through a powerful brain capable of handling even the most difficult situations.

Going inside prisons and jails you meet a lot of people who do not think they are in control. They have given their control over because they are physically incarcerated. They are in prison physically and mentally. What BOSS OF MY BRAIN says is that you can be locked up, you can be told what to do, where to stand, when to sleep, and when to eat, but you cannot, ever, be told what to think while doing so. Your thoughts and how you choose to view a situation is entirely up to you. You choose. You are the boss. No one else dictates how you think, feel or act. That's all you.

BOSS OF MY BRAIN IN ACTION – It was a Wednesday evening at Men's Central Jail in Los Angeles, where there was a weekly GOGI Group being held. One of the group's facilitators was running late, having just returned from court. When he arrived he joined the group, sitting quietly and listening to his peers share about their use of that week's tool. When it was the facilitator's turn to share his thoughts he informed the men that his trial had ended that afternoon. The defense and prosecution had offered their closing statements that day. He said, "I heard things said about me today that I have never heard. They said things about me that I cannot repeat. The things they called me, the type of man they told the jury and the court that I am; it was incredibly difficult to hear those things about myself." He cleared his throat, choked up a bit, and sat up straight in his chair and said, "I'm telling you guys. If I didn't have GOGI and did not know that I am the BOSS OF MY BRAIN, I would not have been able to take that. I could not have heard those things and not wanted to react with my EMOTIONAL PART and OLD HABIT PART. But, I sat there; I remembered I am BOSS OF MY BRAIN. I know better. I am better today. I can do better today. I am not what they say I am. I know who I am today."

Simply, BOSS OF MY BRAIN gave this GOGI student his power. He was in control of how he chose to process information and opinions and how he chose to perceive the world around him, regardless of the negative thoughts or feelings towards him.

GOGI 4 Life!

Coach Carlson

Coach Carlson

GROUP QUESTIONS – BOSS OF MY BRAIN

1. Was there a time today when you used the SMART PART of your brain? Please explain.
2. When do you think you will be tempted to use the OLD HABIT PART?
3. Why do you think some people use the EMOTIONAL PART when something bad happens?
4. What can you do to use the SMART PART more often each day?

GOGI-ism

TOOLS OF THE BODY

Students of GOGI suggested GOGI place the tools into easy-to-memorize groupings. TOOLS OF THE BODY was a grouping created for BOSS OF MY BRAIN, BELLY BREATHING, and FIVE SECOND LIGHTSWITCH. All these tools relate to your control over your body's reactions to life's inevitable challenges.

From Coach Taylor
BOSS OF MY BRAIN

In working with tens of thousands of men and women who have studied GOGI, what I have discovered, and what the GOGI students tell me, is that GOGI is most effective when studied in a group. This group can be as small as two people, but GOGI works best when you can share it, discuss it, support it within your family and with your friends. GOGI is a way of life more than it is a program or a class. It is a way of living.

♡ Coach

Hey Coaches (Taylor & Leigh) & the rest of the GOGI Family

Please accept this gift of gratitude and appreciation for giving us the precious gift of GOGI and a positive way to be of service to our community to help us change the prison culture. I want you to know that we appreciate all of you for believing in us and supporting us in our transformation. We hope that this will help you help others. Thanks again for all that you do.

GOGI for Life

Johnny Crowe

$498.00 in stamps from prisoners!!

Dear GOGI How everyone doing today I hope everyone is doing good. I have completed the GOGI 101 introducing the 12 tools of GOGI. I want to begin by thankyou for helping me change who I am. When I first started the program I was a lost Kid I'm only 23 but I've been thru alot. I never had an opportunity to learn how to control my anger and emotions. With the 12 tools I can not only control my emotions but make them positive ones as well. I hope that one day I can have an chance to go out there and do right and prove to people and myself that theres more to me then meets the eye. Thankyou GOGI for helping me see life in another way for helping me Let Go and Forgive and reminding me I'm the Boss of My Brain. Now if I'm ever angry I use my Five Second Light Switch and remember there are people waiting for me and I help people now because its the right thing todo.

Thankyou GOGI

Jonathan N.

WEEKLY STUDY GUIDE

(Facilitator, when possible, please make a copy of this guide and distribute at the beginning of your meeting. With this guide, students can make certain they are learning the important concepts of this week's tool)

Today's date______________________________

My name________________________________

Please answer all questions. Please feel free to look in your book for the answers, discuss with fellow students, or ask your facilitator.

1) In what SECTION OF TOOLS does this week's tool belong? ______________________________

____

2) What MONTH OF THE YEAR is dedicated to the study of this tool? ____________________

3) What WEEKS OF THE YEAR are dedicated to the study of this tool? ____________________

____

4) What are the KEY WORDS for this tool?

____

____

5) What is the STATEMENT OF OWNERSHIP for this tool? ________________________________

____

____

____

____

____

____

6) Think about a time in your life, either past, present, or future, when this tool might be useful to you. How might you use this tool? __________

____

____

____

____

____

____

____

____

BELLY BREATHING

With BELLY BREATHING I can instantly relax my body and I can make positive decisions. When I am BELLY BREATHING I take control of my thoughts and feelings.

Repeat this week's statement of ownership as often as possible. Before you get out of bed, before your meals, during a break, and before sleeping. Write this statement for added emphasis. Your weekly statement of ownership reinforces this week's tool.

MY GOGI TOOL

BELLY BREATHING

Weeks to study
BELLY BREATHING are:

2nd Week of January

2nd Week of April

2nd Week of July

2nd Week of October

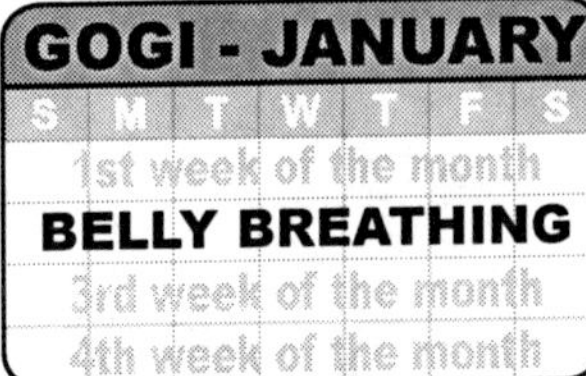

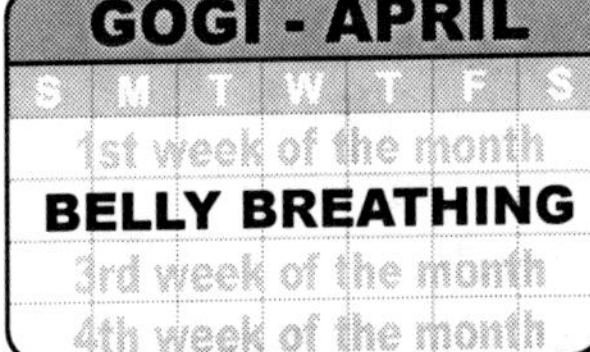

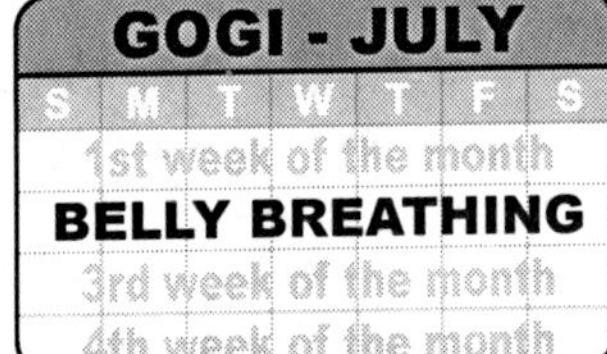

KEY WORDS
BELLY BREATHING

One hand on my chest, one hand on my belly. Which one is moving right now?

MY BRAIN WORKS BETTER WHEN MY BELLY MOVES

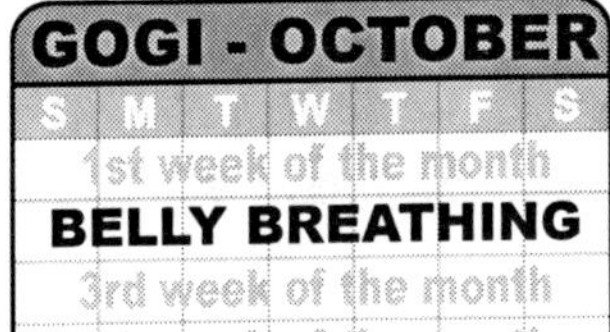

OBJECTIVE – BELLY BREATHING

Your goal in learning this week's tool is to breathe with your chest remaining still and your belly moving in and out. This is your most powerful way to breathe and you can achieve this with this week's tool called BELLY BREATHING.

BELLY BREATHING

WHILE IN THE DORM YOU WILL
BE FACE'D WITH SEVERAL SITUATIONS
INERACTING WITH SO MANY
DIFFERENT PERSONALITY IN ONE
PLACE AND SO WHEN SOME ONE
PUSHES YOUR BUTTONS OR MAKES
YOU ANGRY I'V FOUND THAT
BELLY BREATHING CALMS ME DOWN
A SITUATION IN MY DORM ONE
DAY COULD HAVE REALLY TURN'D ALL BAD
BUT SINCE IV STARTED USEING
TOOLS SUCH AS BELLY BREATHING
& 10 SECOND LIGHT SWITCH
THEISE ALTERNITIVES TO ANY SITUATION
OR ALTERCATION CAN AND DOES
DEFUSE A LOT OF SITUATIONS

A.E. Jr.

AGENDA – BELLY BREATHING

Here is the outline for this week's 90-minute GOGI class/group:

1. Call Your Meeting to Order (1 min)
2. Reading of your GOGI Tools (1 min)
3. Check-in/Recap of Last Week
   A very short recap (10 mins)
4. Check GOGI national calendar
   What is the tool of this week? (1 min)
5. Reading and Activity
   For this tool from this chapter (30 mins)
6. Group Discussions
   Found in this chapter (40-50 mins)
7. Closing Thoughts (1 min)
8. Your GOGI Pledge & Close of Meeting (5 mins)

The twelve (12) tools of GOGI are of value in my life because they have and is continuing to help me tremendously in handling situation(s) appropriately. Whether it be negative self talk, doubt, others negative approachment or just uplifting someone day by showing the awesomeness of how powerful and simple the tools of GOGI are.

Reginald M.

TOOL INTRO – BELLY BREATHING

Did you know that when you breathe with your belly it actually makes you smarter? It is true. This is because when you breathe into your belly you are also getting oxygen into your brain, and that makes the brain work better. GOGI believes there are two types of breathing. There is breathing with your chest and there is BELLY BREATHING.

SO FAR THE GOGI BOOK HAS HELPED ME THROUGH THIS TIME IN MY LIFE. I DEAL WITH THINGS IN A HEALTHIER MANNER. I'M ALSO ABLE TO HELP OTHERS. DAY BY DAY I'M GAINING THE CONFIDENCE I ONCE HAD. I MISSED MYSELF. I LOVE MYSELF. I'M BEGINNING TO FEEL FREE. MORE LIKE ME. THE BEST ME I CAN BE. THIS JOURNEY FOR ME IS JUST BEGINNING. I'M PRACTICING THE PROPER TOOLS I NEED TO, TO LIVE A HAPPY AND POSITIVE LIFE. I'M SO GREATFUL FOR GOGI, EVEN THE PEOPLE I'VE MET HERE.

Alex L.

HOW TO USE – BELLY BREATHING

You can use the BELLY BREATHING tool at any time. Here are three ways to use the tool:

- You can actually put one hand on your chest and one hand on your stomach and see which one is moving.
- Or, just put one hand on your stomach to make sure it is moving.
- And, if you are breathing with your chest, you can direct the air all the way into your stomach area and begin BELLY BREATHING.

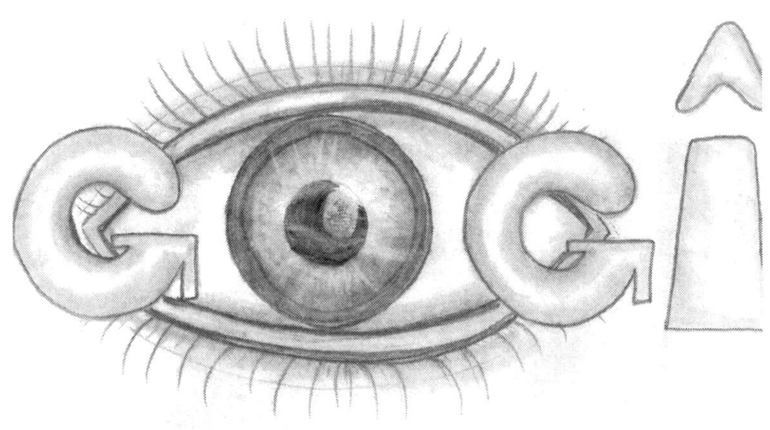

ACTIVITY – BELLY BREATHING

In pairs, small groups, or even by yourself you can enjoy this activity. Standing up makes this activity work even better.

1. Have everyone place one hand on his or her chest. Observe the breathing of your group members. Do you see some people breathing with their chest going up and down?

2. Now have everyone place their other hand on their stomach. Do you see some people breathing with their stomach moving in and out?

3. Have the members of the group point out who is chest breathing and who is BELLY BREATHING. Your goal is that all members of your group use BELLY BREATHING.

Jen B.

REVIEW – BELLY BREATHING

BELLY BREATHING will help you make more positive decisions this is because when you get air into your belly, your brain works better.

The only thing you need to do to use this tool is to ask yourself, which part of your body is getting the air? Are you chest breathing or are you BELLY BREATHING?

Belly Breathing actually works to get over my anxiety anger and stress Behavior.

FEEL THE FLOW

Belly, Breath, Player!

Peer Coach Angel B.

This tool will help us to think in a rational manner and help to prevent us from reacting instinctively according to our normal thought process. WE can learn to use this tool to until it becomes the new, normal reaction to feeling anger and frustration. Rather than acting out or getting aggressive in actions or words, like we are so accustomed to doing, we can reach the place where Belly Breathing is the new norm. Can you imagine how many people would not be hurt by our actions and words? I would like to attain to this.

Darrell L.

From Coach Taylor BELLY BREATHING

Belly Breathing was a tool discovered by men who were so stressed they could barely get air in their chests. I had each one lie down and put one hand on their belly and one on their chest and they stayed there until their belly began to move.

♡ Coach

Thoughts from Coach Leigh Carlson

The GOGI Tool BELLY BREATHING is proper breathing and promotes healthier body and brain function. The benefits of BELLY BREATHING include clarity of thoughts, focus, increased energy, relaxation and an overall healthier brain and body. When your brain and body are getting more oxygen, you are making better and more informed decisions. Every day there are situations that can cause stress and anxiety. It is in these moments that I focus on how I am breathing and it never fails that I am able to combat the anxiety and stress with the use of the GOGI Tool BELLY BREATHING.

BELLY BREATHING helps us avoid conflict and enables us to calm ourselves so we can think more rationally. In working to help implement GOGI at various facilities it always seems at first that people think BELLY BREATHING is silly. However, when people begin to see and feel the benefits of the GOGI Tool BELLY BREATHING, it quickly becomes a part of their every day life. If I had a dollar for every time a man or woman has told me that BELLY BREATHING has kept them out of trouble, conflict or dragged them out of a bout of depression or anxiety, I could buy the whole world a GOGI book; and I would!

BELLY BREATHING IN ACTION –

I think the most powerful examples come from students who share with GOGI how BELLY BREATHING has helped them cope with the pain of situations outside their control. Like the GOGI student who lost his wife to cancer while he was incarcerated; he explained that it was the GOGI Tools that kept him together. It was his ability to control his thoughts, emotions and his use of BELLY BREATHING that kept him stable at a time of great pain. Or the GOGI Peer Coach who received news that his brother had been killed; he shared that in a moment where he thought he would lose control, he sat on his bunk, used his BELLY BREATHING and opened his GOGI book. He was reminded immediately of the tools he needed in that moment to process the information in a productive way no matter how painful the situation.

GOGI 4 Life!

Coach Carlson

Coach Carlson

GOGI-ism

Putting on GOGI GOGGLES

When explaining how his life has changed by becoming a GOGI leader, Peer Coach Angel, said, "Every day I put on my GOGI GOGGLES."

GROUP QUESTIONS – BELLY BREATHING

1. Was there a time today when you realized you were BELLY BREATHING? Please explain.
2. Was there a time today when you realized you were breathing with your chest? Please explain.
3. When do you think you are most likely to breathe with your chest?
4. Why do you think some people breathe with their chest when they are upset?
5. What can you do to use BELLY BREATHING more often each day?

From Coach Taylor
BELLY BREATHING

Many poor decisions and actions you regret later can be stopped with this simple tool called BELLY BREATHING. When you do your BELLY BREATHING you are getting oxygen to your brain. When oxygen gets to your brain you have a better chance of making positive decisions.

Here is a really good tip taught to me by a GOGI Peer Coach. Each time he would get upset, he would quietly put his hand on his belly. That would remind him to do his BELLY BREATHING and it never failed to help him make the next good decision.

♡ Coach

WEEKLY STUDY GUIDE

(Facilitator, when possible, please make a copy of this guide and distribute at the beginning of your meeting. With this guide, students can make certain they are learning the important concepts of this week's tool)

Today's date________________________________

My name_________________________________

Please answer all questions. Please feel free to look in your book for the answers, discuss with fellow students, or ask your facilitator.

1) In what SECTION OF TOOLS does this tool belong? ______________________________

____

2) What MONTH OF THE YEAR is dedicated to the study of this tool? ____________________

3) What WEEKS OF THE YEAR are dedicated to the study of this tool? ____________________

____

4) What are the KEY WORDS for this tool?

____

____

5) What is the STATEMENT OF OWNERSHIP for this tool? ______________________________

____

____

____

____

____

____

6) Think about a time in your life, either past, present, or future, when this tool might be useful to you. How might you use this tool? __________

____

____

____

____

____

____

____

____

FIVE SECOND LIGHTSWITCH

I can flip my FIVE SECOND LIGHTSWITCH and instantly change any negative thought to a positive action. There is no negative thought more powerful than my positive action when I flip my FIVE SECOND LIGHTSWITCH.

Repeat this week's statement of ownership as often as possible. Before you get out of bed, before your meals, during a break, and before sleeping. Write this statement for added emphasis. Your weekly statement of ownership reinforces this week's tool.

MY GOGI TOOL

FIVE SECOND LIGHTSWITCH

Weeks to study FIVE SECOND LIGHTSWITCH are:

3rd Week of January

3rd Week of April

3rd Week of July

3rd Week of October

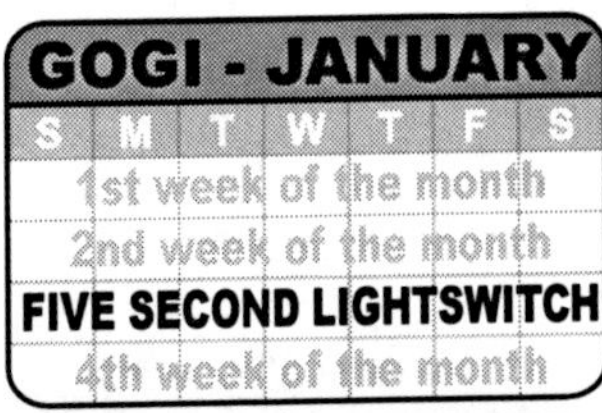

GOGI - APRIL

S M T W T F S

1st week of the month

2nd week of the month

FIVE SECOND LIGHTSWITCH

4th week of the month

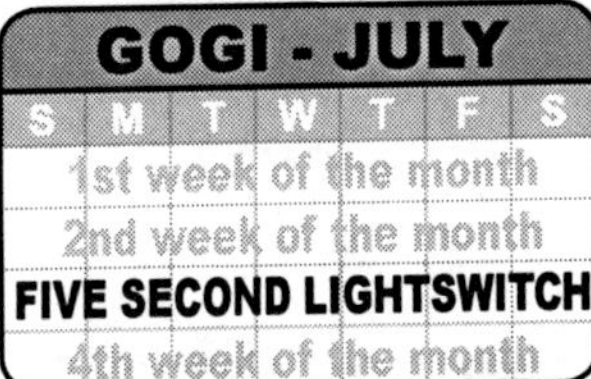

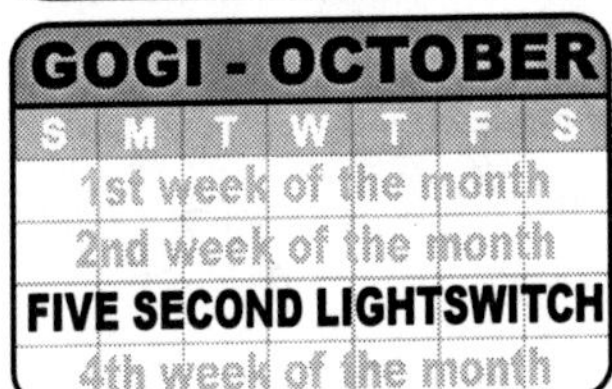

Key Words
FIVE SECOND LIGHTSWITCH

OLD THOUGHT = NEW ACTION

I have an OLD THOUGHT and I have a NEW ACTION

OBJECTIVE – FIVE SECOND LIGHTSWITCH

Your goal this week is to build the new habit of choosing a new positive action every time you have an old negative thought. You can do this by using your FIVE SECOND LIGHTSWITCH, which is this week's tool.

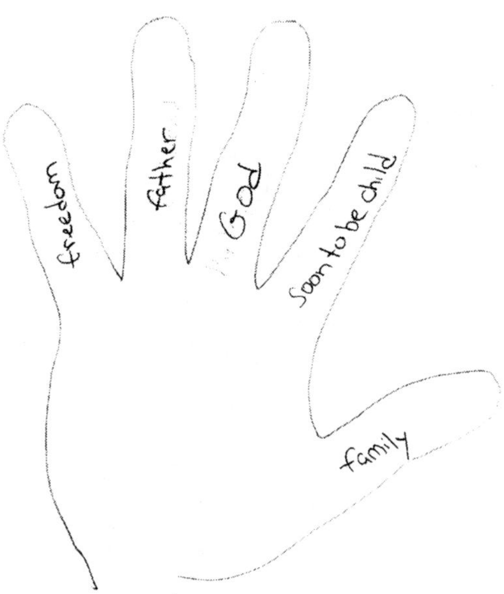

What is your Five-Second Light Switch?

AGENDA – FIVE SECOND LIGHTSWITCH

Here is the outline for this week's 90-minute GOGI class/group:

1. Call Your Meeting to Order (1 min)
2. Reading of your GOGI Tools (1 min)
3. Check-in/Recap of Last Week
   A very short recap (10 mins)
4. Check GOGI national calendar
   What is the tool of this week? (1 min)
5. Reading and Activity
   For this tool from this chapter (30 mins)
6. Group Discussions
   Found in this chapter (40-50 mins)
7. Closing Thoughts (1 min)
8. Your GOGI Pledge & Close of Meeting (5 mins)

The 12 Tools of GOGI are awesome & powerful tools when they are applied to life situations. One of the tools I use the most is BOSS OF MY BRAIN. This tool is so empowering when you think about it. It makes me realize that no one is in charge of me except me! The only way that someone else is in charge of me is if I give them that power, and no matter what, that power is mine and I can take it back if I want to. So ultimately all the choices good & bad that I make in my life are mine & mine alone.

Peer Coach Trevor L.

TOOL INTRO – FIVE SECOND LIGHTSWITCH

Here is an example. When you are told, "just don't think about smoking a cigarette," it seems that all you can think about is the cigarette. When beginning to train your mind to create other thoughts, it is nearly impossible to think that you could simply stop thinking about something that consumed a lot of thinking for a long time.

That is why FIVE SECOND LIGHTSWITCH works; it realizes that your mind has been trained to head down a particular road, almost like autopilot. The GOGI tool FIVE SECOND LIGHTSWITCH permits you to observe that thought, and then replace that thought with a new, more positive and productive action.

At any time, before you do something negative, you can actually send a new message to a different part of your brain and do something more positive. It's like deciding to turn on an alternate light switch in a room, a more positive switch in your brain.

At GOGI we call this flipping the FIVE SECOND LIGHTSWITCH. This tool provides you with the power to reroute your brain activity so you are able to be stronger in your positive choices.

HOW TO USE – FIVE SECOND LIGHTSWITCH

You can use the FIVE SECOND LIGHTSWITCH tool when your thoughts seem to be the boss of you. When an urge seems really really strong, the FIVE SECOND LIGHTSWITCH is a powerful tool to use.

The key to FIVE SECOND LIGHTSWITCH is to have your replacement action ready. If you have your replacement action ready, you are likely to have great success with FIVE SECOND LIGHTSWITCH.

When a thought enters your mind, instead of letting it take over:

> Notice – I notice my thought.
> "Wow. OLD THOUGHT."
>
> New Action – "And I have a NEW ACTION."

Your POSITIVE ACTION is the key to a successful flipping of the FIVE SECOND LIGHTSWITCH. If you are able, you can actually go to a light switch where you are, and this will remind you that you are the boss and can flip the switch inside your brain at any time.

ACTIVITY – FIVE SECOND LIGHTSWITCH

This activity can be a solo, pair, or group activity.

1. **Trouble in my Hand** – Please hold out your hand. Imagine a poor choice sitting in your hand, a poor choice that came from an OLD THOUGHT.
2. **My Five** – Now think of five reasons why you are choosing a new POSITIVE ACTION. Name each reason out loud or to yourself, so that you can hear the five reasons why you want to make a more positive choice. You can count them on your fingers.
3. **Squash the Trouble** – Now make a fist and imagine squashing that OLD THOUGHT and poor choice with your five reasons to make a more positive choice.
4. **My Positive** – What POSITIVE ACTION can you do right now instead?
5. **My New Action** – Do or think about your POSITIVE ACTION.

GOGI-ism

The GOGI Tool Box

It was a car mechanic learning the GOGI Tools who dubbed the phrase "GOGI Tool Box." He felt that he could fix any car with the right tools and believed that if he had his GOGI Tool Box as a kid, he never would have broken down to drugs.

REVIEW – FIVE SECOND LIGHTSWITCH

FIVE SECOND LIGHTSWITCH is widely considered the best of the tools by students who claim they are impulsive, those who claim that sometimes things happen before they even think they had the thought.

People with quick minds and even quicker actions enjoy the fact that GOGI does not hammer in the idea that simply stopping the thought is going to work. It oftentimes does not work for the person with a quick mind and an old habit.

You can think of your thoughts like a series of overhead lights. You get to choose which ones you switch on and which ones you ignore. Remember, no one else is the boss of your brain. FIVE SECOND LIGHTSWITCH can help you build new neural pathways just like an electrician installs a new wire to a light switch.

GOGI-ism

The GOGI Pledge

It was a GOGI Girl who proposed that GOGI have its own pledge, a way to unite the entire world in making more positive choices. The GOGI Pledge was written by Mimi, one of the first GOGI Girls and has been repeated millions of times by GOGI students since that day.

From Coach Taylor
FIVE SECOND LIGHTSWITCH

Remember, the most important part of the FIVE SECOND LIGHTSWITCH tool is that you actually get up and get to a POSITIVE ACTION.

FIVE SECOND LIGHTSWITCH was named by men who were quick to react and sometimes got into trouble before they even knew what they were doing. They said that moving to a positive action was so much easier than trying to stop a thought.

♡ Coach

I have been avoiding confrontations in situations where I would normally end up in trouble. I haven't let old habits control my decision making and I am refraining from emotionally react to situations. When I awake the first thing I do after thanking God is remind myself that I am the Boss of my Brain.

Anthony L.

Thoughts from Coach Leigh Carlson

FIVE SECOND LIGHTSWITCH is like a little miracle in my life and it can be in your life as well. Today, because I have FIVE SECOND LIGHTSWITCH, I am prepared to combat triggers and deal in a healthy way with irritation, anger or stress. I can evaluate alternative POSITIVE ACTIONS and get to those alternative actions in order to refrain from reacting in a way that is not my very best.

FIVE SECOND LIGHTSWITCH is helpful for everything from starting your day off on the right foot to avoiding conflict throughout the day. With your FIVE SECOND LIGHTSWITCH you are focused on getting to a POSITIVE ACTION and the negative thoughts simply become less powerful. I put FIVE SECOND LIGHTSWITCH into action when I feel overwhelmed or if my thoughts are not productive. I give myself POSITIVE THOUGHTS, which affirm that my goal for the day is to be my very best. Every action I take that day will be positive, because I have a FIVE SECOND LIGHTSWITCH. I can flip the switch, get rid of the negative and get to a positive action. When people are impulsive or reactionary and don't take the time to think about our responses or reactions and measure the possible outcome, changing that behavior can seem nearly impossible. But, it is not. You can rewire your brain and you can begin to react differently to situations that have previously caused you harm or harm to others.

FIVE SECOND LIGHTSWITCH IN ACTION -

I was reviewing coursework from a student housed on a maximum-security prison yard and he was explaining how he was using the GOGI Tool FIVE SECOND LIGHTSWITCH each day to pay attention to how he reacted to various situations in his environment in a way he believed to be more productive. He shared a particularly interesting story about his interaction with a correctional officer. He was heading out of his building on the way to the yard. He was not looking where he was going and ran straight into a correctional officer heading from the yard into the building where he was housed. He was not sure who he ran into, but admitted that in the past he would have simply fired off at the mouth or worse. In this case, he said he thought of his GOGI Tool FIVE SECOND LIGHTSWITCH, he paused, stepped back and looked up to see the correctional officer in front of him; he thought to himself – this could end badly. He smiled and apologized. The officer let him pass and he proceeded to the yard to get his workout in.

He added that the correctional officer apologized to him as well. This is how you take control of your situation. You decide how you react and what actions you take to redirect your life and the course of any situation. Had he immediately reacted like in the past, things would have ended very differently.

GOGI 4 Life!

Coach Carlson

Coach Carlson

GROUP QUESTIONS – FIVE SECOND LIGHTSWITCH

1. Was there a time today when you realized you needed to use the GOGI tool FIVE SECOND LIGHTSWITCH? Please explain.

2. Was there a time today when your thoughts were automatic and you struggled to control your thoughts or actions? Please explain.

3. When do you think you are most likely to need to flip the FIVE SECOND LIGHTSWITCH?

4. Why do you think some people act before they think?

5. What can you do to use FIVE SECOND LIGHTSWITCH more often each day?

GOGI Girls of FCI Dublin, CA

WEEKLY STUDY GUIDE

(Facilitator, when possible, please make a copy of this guide and distribute at the beginning of your meeting. With this guide, students can make certain they are learning the important concepts of this week's tool)

Today's date______________________________

My name______________________________

Please answer all questions. Please feel free to look in your book for the answers, discuss with fellow students, or ask your facilitator.

1) In what SECTION OF TOOLS does this tool belong? ______________________________

   ____

2) What MONTH OF THE YEAR is dedicated to the study of this tool? ____________________

3) What WEEKS OF THE YEAR are dedicated to the study of this tool? ____________________

   ____

4) What are the KEY WORDS for this tool?

   ____

   ____

5) What is the STATEMENT OF OWNERSHIP for this tool? ____________________

____

____

____

____

____

____

6) Think about a time in your life, either past, present, or future, when this tool might be useful to you. How might you use this tool? __________

____

____

____

____

____

____

____

____

Testimonial by Coach Tevita Niu

Coach Tevita

When I first heard the name Getting Out By Going In and GOGI it was when I was attending a life skills program offered at the Oxbow jail of the Salt Lake County Sheriff's Department. I was in my county uniform with a wristband on, again. It was not my first time locked up, but this time was different.

I am writing this, because I know through personal experience how well the GOGI TOOLS FOR POSITIVE DECISION MAKING work, not only in my life, but in the lives of the men I was lucky enough to Coach as I worked my way up the LEVELS OF LEARNING and became a Certified Coach, even while I was locked up.

What I found interesting about GOGI, and what had me so curious, was the men in the group were holding GOGI meetings way after lock down, long after all the programs were done and most staff had gone home. I began attending these GOGI meetings held during the graveyard shift and I was issued a GOGI book the facility had purchased for inmates wanting to attend this volunteer, after hours, inmate facilitated group of men learning simple tools for positive decision making.

I was willing to try anything, because I was finally tired of making wrong choices that put me in lock up. I was tired of trying to blame it on drugs and addiction. I was tired of being tired and I was ready for a real change. It was when I started reading the GOGI BOOK and attending Graveyard Shift GOGI that I started to feed my desire to change my life.

The material in the GOGI book was different from every other program, because the material made sense and it was developed by prisoners just like me, for other prisoners just like me. In the beginning it was discouraging, because my peers were teasing and making fun of me being the "super programmer" inmate because I would choose to read and study the GOGI book instead of playing cards or going out for recreation when we were permitted to get out of our cells and move around in a bigger

space. I just wanted, I needed, to feed my brain the information in the GOGI book that seemed so simple, but information that was delivered in such a way that I really knew was going to help me make the change. It was information I had been missing all my life.

I continued to attend the GOGI meetings that were held every Monday, Wednesday, and Friday night. It was a bit challenging going to these meetings late at night while attending the other life skills programming offered by the jail during the day, but the Oxbow Jail was a programming facility and the only way you could stay there was if you got up in the morning and attended life skills. With the flack I was getting from the guys and with the pressure I was getting from the life skills part of my stay, I would have normally given up. I would have said it was not worth it. I would have blamed someone for something and gone back to the old me, wanting change, but not being able to make it through the politicking and practicing of a new way of being. But through it all, I survived and was successful in graduating the life skills class by using the GOGI TOOLS that I was learning long after the noise of the day was turned off and the graveyard shift officers permitted our GOGI Group.

The tools were easily presented. Four sections. They are: TOOLS OF THE BODY, TOOLS OF CHOICE, TOOLS OF MOVING FORWARD and TOOLS OF CREATION. The first set of tools, TOOLS OF THE BODY made sense to me because it simplified how my body acted, reacted, and thought. Knowing more about my body, the TOOLS OF CHOICE became fun and I could easily practice the positive tools in that section. These two sections made the TOOLS OF MOVING FORWARD easier for me and I could finally walk beyond the limits of my past with confidence. That was the fun part, because I could see, finally, that I did have a choice and I had the ability to use the tools to begin creating and being the new me, the better version I had always wanted to be. The new me is the best version of who I always was deep inside, but didn't know how to become on my own.

The new me is my dream of being solid and strong put into action as a result of using the GOGI TOOLS FOR POSITIVE DECISION MAKING. And, I am happy to say, I am still getting better and better, and more of my dreams are unfolding each day in my life.

Learning the GOGI TOOLS FOR POSITIVE DECISION MAKING has been the game-changer in my life. I live, eat and breathe GOGI, even now that I am no longer in jails and prisons with a number. With my family I talk GOGI, I continue to volunteer to teach GOGI, I make my decisions using the tools and I am a living and breathing example of just how simple using the tools in your life can become.

I am 100 percent GOGI. I will always continue to learn and grow in living my life The GOGI Way, so I just keep getting better, happier, and more internally and externally free. I always wanted to be a good father and now I AM. I always wanted to live a free and happy life and now I AM. I always wanted to be spiritually closer to my creator and now I AM. I always wanted to be an example of a leader for good and now I AM. I have no doubt that if you truly invest the time and energy like I invested, your dreams of being the best version of you will become your daily reality.

In this book you will find and learn the answers, just as I did. It may be difficult to be consistent, just do it. It may be challenging when others tease you, just do it. It may be emotionally difficult to deal with the past, just do it. It might be frightening to deal with the future, just do it. Don't let anything or anyone stand in your way of using these tools. I am here to say that all you have been searching for is right here in your hands. The GOGI TOOLS FOR POSITIVE DECISION MAKING are for you to help you realize internal happiness and the freedom that is possible when you put the tools to use.

I can confidently say this because I am Coach Tevita Niu and I am GOGI 4 Life!

Coach Tevita

SECTION TWO:

Teach Me How to GOGI

TOOLS OF CHOICE

POSITIVE THOUGHTS
POSITIVE WORDS
POSITIVE ACTIONS

STATEMENT OF OWNERSHIP
POSITIVE THOUGHTS

POSITIVE THOUGHTS

My POSITIVE THOUGHTS set the direction of my life from this moment forward. I focus on POSITIVE THOUGHTS, even when it is difficult or challenging. No matter what is happening, I can create POSITIVE THOUGHTS.

Repeat this week's statement of ownership as often as possible. Before you get out of bed, before your meals, during a break, and before sleeping. Write this statement for added emphasis. Your weekly statement of ownership reinforces this week's tool.

MY GOGI TOOL

POSITIVE THOUGHTS

Weeks to study
POSITIVE THOUGHTS are:

4th Week of January

4th Week of April

4th Week of July

4th Week of October

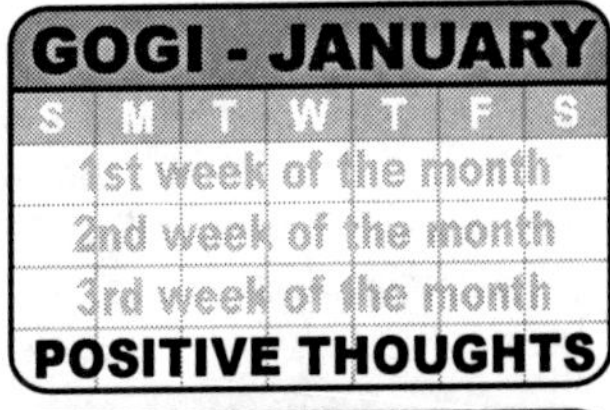

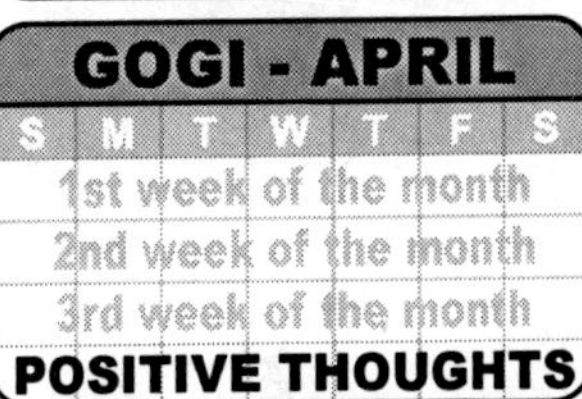

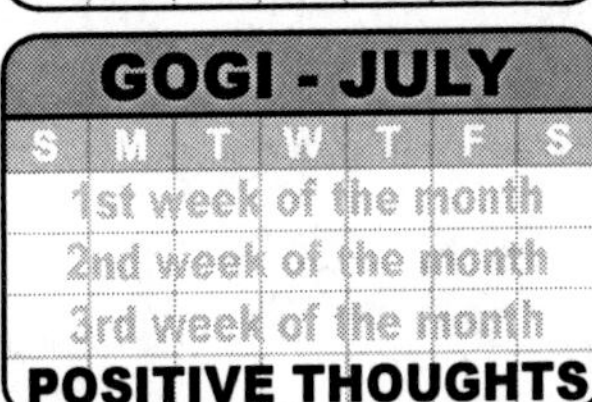

KEY WORDS
POSITIVE THOUGHTS

THE THREE P's

Is it POWERFUL?

Is it PRODUCTIVE?

Is it POSITIVE?

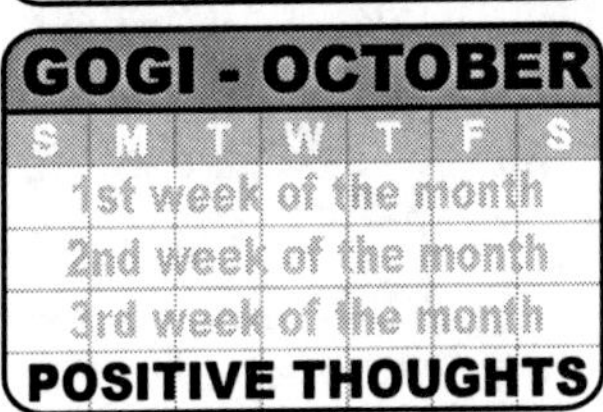

OBJECTIVE – POSITIVE THOUGHTS

Your goal with this week's tool is to practice being the boss of your thinking and to choose thoughts that are POWERFUL, PRODUCTIVE and POSITIVE. You will practice this with the tool POSITIVE THOUGHTS.

After completing the course myself, I realized the amazing and positive impact this course has on my life as well as other's who have made participated in it. The biggest impact this program has had on me has been changing my perception towards life and, addressing the issues that come with it in a more positive manner. I truly believe that these tools are instrumental in Reshaping an individuals life, giving them a second chance with a momentum of positive motivation behind it. I personally want to thank you and, the program for allowing me the further opportunity towards progress as a facilitator. My only hope is that I can impact my students lives with your program as much as your program has impacted mine

Roberto H.

GOGI-ism

TOOLS OF CHOICE

Students of GOGI suggested that POSITIVE THOUGHTS, POSITIVE WORDS and POSITIVE ACTIONS be grouped into a section of tools called TOOLS OF CHOICE. The "Positives" as they are commonly called, are all related to your choice in how you respond to life's inevitable challenges.

AGENDA – POSITIVE THOUGHTS

Here is the outline for this week's 90-minute GOGI class/group:

1. Call Your Meeting to Order (1 min)
2. Reading of your GOGI Tools (1 min)
3. Check-in/Recap of Last Week
   A very short recap (10 mins)
4. Check GOGI national calendar
   What is the tool of this week? (1 min)
5. Reading and Activity
   For this tool from this chapter. (30 mins)
6. Group Discussions
   Found in this chapter (40-50 mins)
7. Closing Thoughts (1 min)
8. Your GOGI Pledge & Close of Meeting (5 mins)

WHEN I GET NEGATIVE THOUGHTS I INSTANTLY SHUT IT OFF WITH THE REALITY THAT MY THOUGHTS HAVE POWER AND BY ENTERTAINING AND PONDERING ANYTHING NEGATIVE, I AM OPENING THE DOOR FOR IT TO MANIFEST ITSELF WITHIN MY LIFE. I CHOOSE TO UNLOCK THE DOOR TO POSITIVITY, WHICH WILL NOT ONLY MAKE ME FEEL BETTER, BUT EVERYONE THAT I INTERACT WITH.

Peer Coach David R.

TOOL INTRO – POSITIVE THOUGHTS

You are the boss of your brain and you can create any thought you want to create. When you force your brain to create POSITIVE THOUGHTS you are actually using the tool POSITIVE THOUGHTS.

Your brain will follow your orders and if you use the tool POSITIVE THOUGHTS over and over again, eventually your brain will begin to create POSITIVE THOUGHTS on its own.

Gordon K.

HOW TO USE – POSITIVE THOUGHTS

You can use POSITIVE THOUGHTS by considering your thoughts and asking yourself, "Is this thought POWERFUL? Is it PRODUCTIVE? Is it POSITIVE?"

When you ask yourself these three questions, you will become more in control of your thoughts.

THE THREE P'S

- Is it POWERFUL?
- Is it PRODUCTIVE?
- Is it POSITIVE?

If the answer is no, then pick a more POSITIVE THOUGHT.

I would say that if you want to relieve stress and clear your mind, you have to change your thinking. Don't you notice the difference when you're thinking positive than when you're thinking negative? In my experience by always using positive thoughts my life has been uplifting, people can tell they are in better moods. My thinking has never been clearer. No stress and I embrace POSITIVE THOUGHTS

Antonio G.

ACTIVITY – POSITIVE THOUGHTS

Think about your day today.
Then consider the THREE P's.

- Is it POWERFUL?
- Is it PRODUCTIVE?
- Is it POSITIVE?

In small groups, spend 5 minutes where you share POWERFUL, PRODUCTIVE and POSITIVE thoughts with your group members.

Remember, only POWERFUL, PRODUCTIVE and POSITIVE thoughts are to be shared. Sounds simple? It's not quite as simple as it seems and it may seem strange to try to find something positive about a negative situation, but POSITIVE THOUGHTS are your key to change.

Here is another activity: have one person state a situation that might be considered negative. Each group member states one positive thought about that situation.

IT AINT THE TRIALS WE FACE THAT BREAKS US MENTALLY/EMOTIONALLY.ITS HOW WE WERE CONDITIONED 2 COPE WITH SUCH ADVERSITIES THAT BECOMES OUR DOWNFALLS.

Jason – San Quentin, SP

From Coach Taylor
POSITIVE THOUGHTS

POSITIVE THOUGHTS was the tool designed by women in jail who told me that until they could create POWERFUL, PRODUCTIVE and POSITIVE THOUGHTS, they were doomed to struggle, as well as endure depression and feelings of hopelessness.

What is so amazing is just how quickly struggle goes away when we create POSITIVE THOUGHTS. This tool is like a big eraser to wipe away years of pain.

♡ Coach

GOGI-ism

THE OFFICIAL GOGI MEETING FORMAT

Wanting a more standardized way to unite anyone studying GOGI, the first group of GOGI Girls created the "Official GOGI Meeting Format" which they suggested be used anytime 2 or more people assemble to study their GOGI Tools.

REVIEW – POSITIVE THOUGHTS

POSITIVE THOUGHTS are yours to create and they can become a natural habit if you practice them enough. Until they become a habit you simply review your thoughts. Ask yourself THE THREE P's:

Is it POWERFUL?

Is it PRODUCTIVE?

Is it POSITIVE?

If it does not meet the "THREE P's" then pick another thought.

GOGI is a self-help program that offer me a door of opportunity to learn how to use my mind on a more productive and a positive level in life. GOGI provides the tools that helps me learn that I am the "BOSS OF MY BRAIN" and CLAIM RESPONSIBILITY for my past actions. And also, GOGI teach me to "LET GO" of my past things that held me back from growing into a better person, a better human being and a better example. GOGI means to me is like listening to your favorite love song that motivate you to treat the one you love better in life ☺.

DARIN 2014

Thoughts from Coach Leigh Carlson

How you think about your life and your situation dictates whether you are in prison or not, happy or not, at peace or not. Positivity and negativity are contagious and both can spread quickly. The GOGI Tool POSITIVE THOUGHTS was the game changer for me. I struggled with negative thoughts and used negative words my whole life to describe myself, others and situations. I was very rarely happy. I did not realize the power that a change in thought would have on my life. I did not realize that I chose to think of a situation in a specific way, and that I could change that thought, even about a negative situation, to something POWERFUL, PRODUCTIVE and POSITIVE. Changing my thoughts about how I view others, and myself, as well as every situation in my life, has completely transformed how I value my life and the lives of others. POSITIVE THOUGHTS have been a key to my internal freedom.

POSITIVE THOUGHTS IN ACTION –

At a federal jail, there was a student that was committed to starting GOGI in his unit and to helping others begin groups in separate units. His POSITIVE THOUGHTS were that sharing the GOGI Tools with others would create a better environment for everyone. When we received

By thinking positive I give myself a greater chance of being successful it gives me a feeling of happiness inside and it helps prepare me for obstacles that I encounter.

Anthony L.

a letter from one of his GOGI men stating that GOGI was an active group on every unit and that the word "GOGI" had become the word used in his housing unit when someone needed to avoid a potential conflict, we could not help but acknowledge what his POSITIVE THOUGHTS had helped create. When someone on the unit would get upset, when things would get heated, when conflict arose, the GOGI men would simply say, "GOGI" and walk away. It reminded them immediately that they have choices, and tools with which to make those choices positive. One man's POSITIVE THOUGHTS brought peace to a tense and hostile Federal pre-trial jail unit. Amazing. See if you can follow his example.

GOGI 4 Life!

Coach Carlson

Coach Carlson

GoGI has grown and changed so many people here in this institution and I'm really happy and Proud to be part of it.

God bless You and thank You for everything you have done for me and many others, that like myself, were looking for a change.

GoGI 4 Life!

Carlos A.

GROUP QUESTIONS – POSITIVE THOUGHTS

1. Was there a time today when you used more POSITIVE THOUGHTS than usual? Please explain.
2. Was there a time today when you could have asked if your thoughts were POWERFUL, PRODUCTIVE and POSITIVE? Please explain.
3. When do you think you are most likely to need to use POSITIVE THOUGHTS?
4. Why do you think some people find POSITIVE THOUGHTS difficult?
5. What can you do to be using POSITIVE THOUGHTS more often each day?

When I first started GOGI I thought it was like all programs. But, as I learned that I control my thoughts, words and actions because I am BOSS OF MY BRAIN. And I can change my old habits by LETTING GO. With REALITY CHECK I can always know that nobody is perfect and regardless of how bad I'm doing we can always check my progress with the 10 and 2 rule. I now look at life different. Instead of the glass being half empty, it is half full.

Thomas B.

WEEKLY STUDY GUIDE

(Facilitator, when possible, please make a copy of this guide and distribute at the beginning of your meeting. With this guide, students can make certain they are learning the important concepts of this week's tool)

Today's date______________________________

My name________________________________

Please answer all questions. Please feel free to look in your book for the answers, discuss with fellow students, or ask your facilitator.

1) In what SECTION OF TOOLS does this tool belong? ____________________________

   ____

2) What MONTH OF THE YEAR is dedicated to the study of this tool? __________________

3) What WEEKS OF THE YEAR are dedicated to the study of this tool? __________________

   ____

4) What are the KEY WORDS for this tool?

   ____

   ____

5) What is the STATEMENT OF OWNERSHIP for this tool? ____

____

____

____

____

____

____

6) Think about a time in your life, either past, present, or future, when this tool might be useful to you. How might you use this tool? __________

____

____

____

____

____

____

____

____

POSITIVE WORDS

My POSITIVE WORDS tell the world what I am thinking and who I am today. I use POSITIVE WORDS to break free from my past and move forward into a positive future.

Repeat this week's statement of ownership as often as possible. Before you get out of bed, before your meals, during a break, and before sleeping. Write this statement for added emphasis. Your weekly statement of ownership reinforces this week's tool.

MY GOGI TOOL

POSITIVE WORDS

Weeks to study POSITIVE WORDS are:

1st Week of February

1st Week of May

1st Week of August

1st Week of November

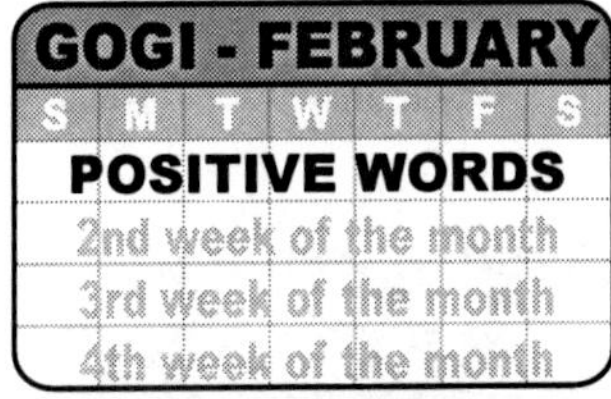

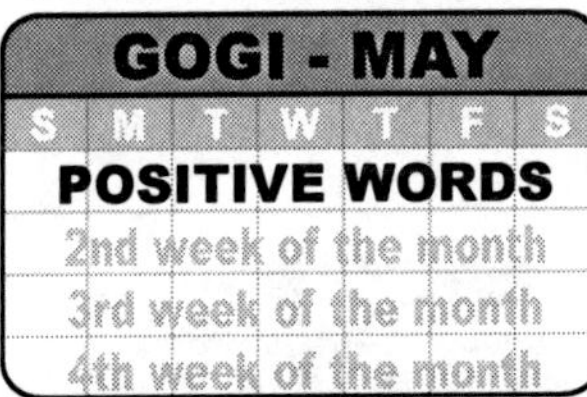

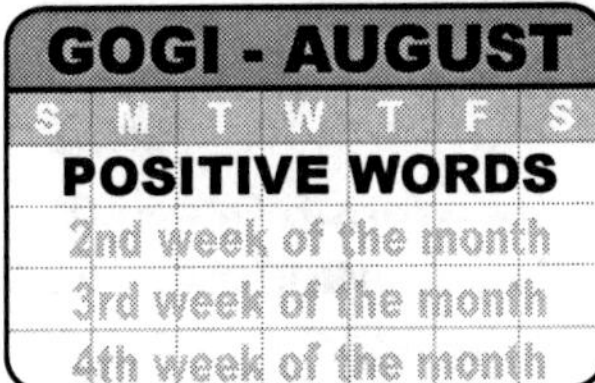

KEY WORDS
POSITIVE WORDS

THE THREE P's

- Is it POWERFUL?
- Is it PRODUCTIVE?
- Is it POSITIVE?

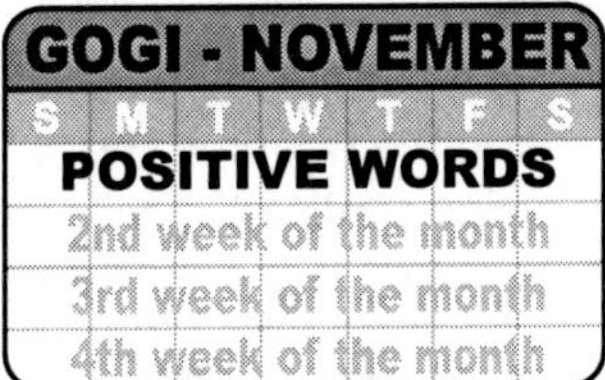

OBJECTIVE – POSITIVE WORDS

Your goal this week is to practice being the boss of the words you choose. You will choose words that are POWERFUL, PRODUCTIVE and POSITIVE when you learn the tool POSITIVE WORDS.

As humans, we usually choose the same words we did yesterday. How can we expect change when our words remain the same?

♡ Coach

GOGI-ism

GOGI University

It was a man in prison in a small solitary cell who stated that he had founded his own GOGI UNIVERSITY. Over every inch of his small space he posted GOGI pages, GOGI handouts, GOGI drawings.

A prison cell, dayroom, chow hall, gymnasium, or even inside your own mind you can create your own GOGI University. All it takes is to move through your day with your tools at the forefront of every experience. Every day you can be enrolled in the GOGI University.

AGENDA – POSITIVE WORDS

Here is the outline for this week's 90-minute GOGI class/group:

1. Call Your Meeting to Order (1 min)
2. Reading of your GOGI Tools (1 min)
3. Check-in/Recap of Last Week
   A very short recap (10 mins)
4. Check GOGI national calendar
   What is the tool of this week? (1 min)
5. Reading and Activity
   For this tool from this chapter (30 mins)
6. Group Discussions
   Found in this chapter (40-50 mins)
7. Closing Thoughts (1 min)
8. Your GOGI Pledge & Close of Meeting (5 mins)

I'm learning to choose the positive words and focus on how to apply in a positive way. I remain quite if I cannot speak Positive words. The transformation is remarkable. I'm able to communicate other people in a proper way. These are the positive things that transform in a short period of time. I also check myself every now and then. I correct my mistake always to avoid any conflict towards other people.

Gilbert A.

TOOL INTRO – POSITIVE WORDS

Did you know that the words you choose tell the world quite a lot about you? Your words tell others what you are thinking, how you think, and if you are generally a positive or negative person.

POSITIVE WORDS have a powerful way of attracting POSITIVE ACTIONS, therefore getting in the habit of choosing more POSITIVE WORDS puts you in charge of how the world sees you and how you see yourself, which increases your POSITIVE ACTIONS automatically.

Negative words usually have the word "not" included in them. Words like "can not," and "will not" or "could not" and "is not" are negative words. There is a bunch of other "not" words and they are negative words. Rather than picking a word with a "not" you can pick words that are POWERFUL, PRODUCTIVE and POSITIVE.

When you train your brain to seek out and support POSITIVE WORDS, you will notice more positive things begin to happen in your life. Is that coincidence? No. Like attracts like. If you are negative, you will attract more negative. If you are positive, somehow, magically, good things will eventually come your way. Don't underestimate the power of POSITIVE WORDS.

HOW TO USE – POSITIVE WORDS

You can use POSITIVE WORDS by asking yourself the THREE P's. Are your words POWERFUL? Are they PRODUCTIVE? Are they POSITIVE? You can test to see if others are using POSITIVE WORDS by asking yourself if their words are POWERFUL, PRODUCTIVE and POSITIVE.

Before you choose your words, test them out with the THREE P's. Are your words POWERFUL? PRODUCTIVE? POSITIVE?

6-27-14 Pg. 6 Learning to strengthen and change the world around me by changing the way I talk is an amazing thing to me. Tibel said on the 23rd, the more ~~positive words~~ POSITIVE WORDS I put out there, the less room there is for the negative ones.

Erica W.

GOGI-ism

GOGI-fied

To be GOGI-fied means that you start using the GOGI TOOLS because others around you are living THE GOGI WAY. You don't even need to be "GOGI" to start acting "GOGI". That is what it means to be GOGI-fied.

ACTIVITY – POSITIVE WORDS

In small groups, pairs, or by yourself, this activity will help you identify your easiest and most common POSITIVE WORDS.

1. Have each group member pick out their five favorite POSITIVE WORDS.
2. Have them use these words to describe something about today.
3. Have them use these words to describe tomorrow.
4. Have them use these words to describe the past.
5. As a group, discuss how these words might help you be positive each day.

We had one group member stand in the center of the group circle as each and every group member randomly got up, faced him, and "Positively" expressed his experience of that person. After the standing member had received words from everyone, he picks the next group member to stand in the center of the group circle, and the entire process is repeated until each group member has had the opportunity to express and receive these positive accolades. When the exercise is complete, we give the members the opportunity to express their experience with the exercise. I have seen walls "torn" down. Most say, they have never had these Positive Words spoken to them before

Peer Coach Malcolm C.

Here is an option for another activity:

1. Have one member of the group stand in the middle of the circle.
2. One at a time, have the members of the group say something positive about this person.
3. Have someone write down what is said and present this to the person when everyone is finished.
4. As a group, discuss what you think and how you feel saying and hearing positive words about a person.

GOGI-ism

I am THE B.O.M.B.

This phrase was first written in a letter to GOGI from a woman who had never felt in control of her life. In her letter she stated I am THE BOMB – BOSS OF MY BRAIN! You can be THE BOMB, too.

REVIEW – POSITIVE WORDS

POSITIVE WORDS is your tool to direct conversations and situations so they are positive and support your success.

By steering your vocabulary to the positive, its like steering your car directly toward your intended destination.

POSITIVE WORDS will diffuse an argument, open up opportunities, squash a beef, and bring you added peace. Just ask yourself, are these words POWERFUL, PRODUCTIVE and POSITIVE. The THREE P's will not let you down.

And, even when you face negative situations, POSITIVE WORDS permits you an uncommon control over the outcome. You no longer need to be the victim of circumstance. You can create the outcome you desire with POSITIVE WORDS.

GOGI-ism

GOGI ON THE GO

One GOGI student stated that it helped to write down the tools and put them in his pocket. In this way, he said, he could use GOGI ON THE GO. When you create a way to take GOGI with you through your day, you are creating your own way to have GOGI ON THE GO!

From Coach Taylor
POSITIVE WORDS

POSITIVE WORDS was a tool designed by women in jail. I told them that the more they chose negative words, the more negativity they were creating in their lives. They decided that it was not enough to say you have POSITIVE THOUGHTS without putting them into POSITIVE WORDS. Your choice of words tells the world what you think, how you think, and what you believe. Do you really want others hearing complaints? Negativity? And judgements? Negativity rarely helps to fix the problem, anyway. Don't you prefer hearing someone when they are speaking about positive things? Encouraging others? Helping with a thoughtful word or two? You can become more positive about your entire life when you begin to choose more POSITIVE WORDS.

♡ Coach

GOGI-ism

The GOGI FAMILY

In the hundreds of letters GOGI receives from men and women in prisons and jails, they often state they feel as if GOGI is a family of all sorts of people who all want to make more positive decisions in their lives. Yep. That is correct. GOGI is one big positive decision-making family.

Thoughts from Coach Leigh Carlson

I am grateful today for the gift of POSITIVE WORDS. Words are powerful and have the ability to encourage or discourage, lift up or tear down a human being. POSITIVE WORDS can change the course of a conversation and a life and have given me the power to be a force for good and a light in the lives of others.

POSITIVE WORDS IN ACTION –

As I sat with a GOGI Group one evening, a particularly involved facilitator was uncharacteristically quiet. Eventually when the group came to a brief pause, he said "Coach. I want to thank you for coming here to be with us and for supporting GOGI here. We need this. GOGI has helped a lot of men. I promise you, I will take GOGI with me to prison. I received a sentence of life without the possibility of parole, but I am not giving up. I can use my time to help others and be of service."

The men in the group, each took a moment to offer him a kind word. Often poor choices seem to be how others define you. To have the knowledge that you have your own POSITIVE WORDS and that you can use them to define yourself is what keeps us moving in the right direction. We grow and transform when we use our POSITIVE WORDS. We can become new and find new and POSITIVE WORDS to describe our situation, ourselves and others.

GOGI 4 Life!

Coach Carlson

Coach Carlson

GROUP QUESTIONS – POSITIVE WORDS

1. Was there a time today when you used POSITIVE WORDS? Please explain.
2. Was there a time today when it was difficult to use POSITIVE WORDS? Please explain.
3. When someone near you is negative is it difficult for you to maintain POSITIVE WORDS? Please explain.
4. Why do you think some people do not use POSITIVE WORDS?
5. What can you do to use POSITIVE WORDS more often each day?

GOGI-ism

GOGI GUMBO

GOGI student David F. stated that "GOGI is a family, mixed with all kinds of stuff – everyone from all colors, sizes, beliefs, ages, everything. We all come together and we all are GOGI." That is how GOGI GUMBO got its name.

WEEKLY STUDY GUIDE

(Facilitator, when possible, please make a copy of this guide and distribute at the beginning of your meeting. With this guide, students can make certain they are learning the important concepts of this week's tool)

Today's date______________________________

My name______________________________

Please answer all questions. Please feel free to look in your book for the answers, discuss with fellow students, or ask your facilitator.

1) In what SECTION OF TOOLS does this tool belong? ______________________________

____

2) What MONTH OF THE YEAR is dedicated to the study of this tool? ____________________

3) What WEEKS OF THE YEAR are dedicated to the study of this tool? ____________________

____

4) What are the KEY WORDS for this tool?

____

____

5) What is the STATEMENT OF OWNERSHIP for this tool? ___________________________

____

____

____

____

____

____

6) Think about a time in your life, either past, present, or future, when this tool might be useful to you. How might you use this tool? __________

____

____

____

____

____

____

____

____

POSITIVE ACTIONS

I know I have the power to transform my world through my POSITIVE ACTIONS. I choose my POSITIVE ACTIONS so I can move beyond my past and create my positive future.

Repeat this week's statement of ownership as often as possible. Before you get out of bed, before your meals, during a break, and before sleeping. Write this statement for added emphasis. Your weekly statement of ownership reinforces this week's tool.

MY GOGI TOOL

POSITIVE ACTIONS

Weeks to study POSITIVE ACTIONS are:

2nd Week of February

2nd Week of May

2nd Week of August

2nd Week of November

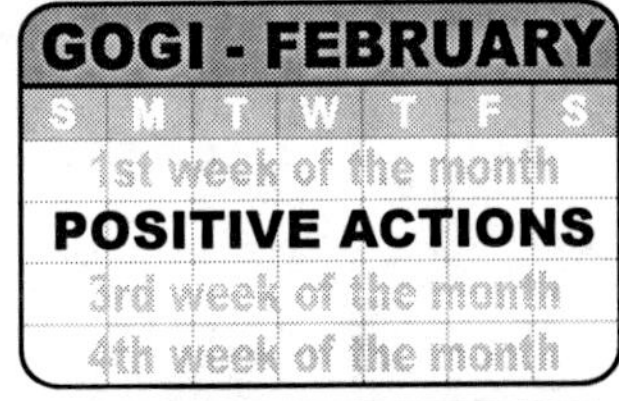

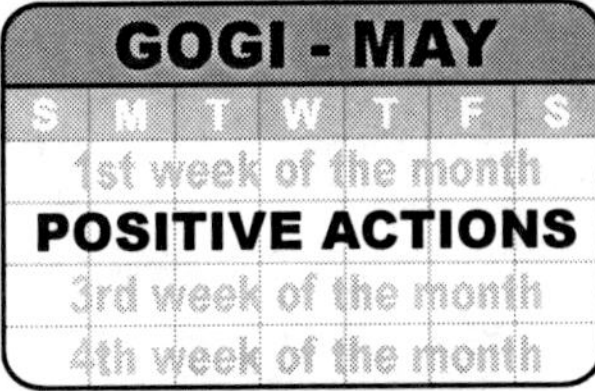

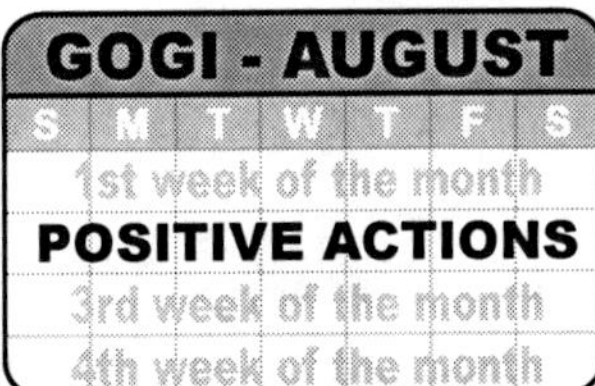

KEY WORDS
POSITIVE ACTIONS

THE THREE P's

Is it POWERFUL?
Is it PRODUCTIVE?
Is it POSITIVE?

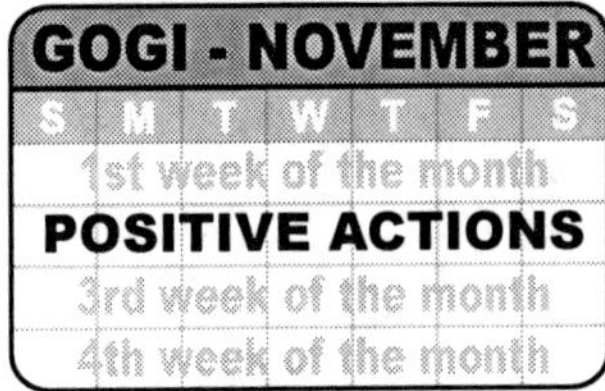

OBJECTIVE – POSITIVE ACTIONS

Your goal this week is to be the boss of all your actions.

You will choose actions that are POWERFUL, PRODUCTIVE and POSITIVE when you learn the tool POSITIVE ACTIONS.

small things keep me focused on my growth and lasting change. POSITIVE ACTIONS heals me on the inside while I am being a roll model and trying to do good for the world around me. Me doing one small POSITIVE ACTIONS can make someone elses day or week so much better with out ever even knowing it.

Ronald K.

GOGI-ism

GROWING UP GOGI

When you learn GOGI, it is natural to want all your loved ones to learn GOGI, too. More and more parents are teaching their children GOGI TOOLS. When you are GROWING UP GOGI, you are learning GOGI from day one.

AGENDA – POSITIVE ACTIONS

Here is the outline for this week's 90-minute GOGI class/group:

1. Call Your Meeting to Order (1 min)
2. Reading of your GOGI Tools (1 min)
3. Check-in/Recap of Last Week
   A very short recap (10 mins)
4. Check GOGI national calendar
   What is the tool of this week? (1 min)
5. Reading and Activity
   For this tool from this chapter (30 mins)
6. Group Discussions
   Found in this chapter (40-50 mins)
7. Closing Thoughts (1 min)
8. Your GOGI Pledge & Close of Meeting (5 mins)

GOGI-ism

OMGOGI!!

Everyone has heard the abbreviation or catch phrase – OMG! In this case it stands for OMGOGI!!! It is most commonly used when sharing another amazing GOGI story!

TOOL INTRO – POSITIVE ACTIONS

Did you know that just doing one small POSITIVE ACTION may have a big positive result in your day? Yes, that is correct, even one small POSITIVE ACTION each day can help you a great deal in your ability to be the boss of your life.

POSITIVE ACTIONS are the small things you do, not necessarily the big things. The smaller POSITIVE ACTIONS are actually more powerful, because you can do more of them each day.

Did you know that if you have 2-3 POSITIVE ACTIONS picked out ahead of time, it is easier to overcome urges to make a poor decision?

If you consider the things you did yesterday, you can list those things which were positive. You can also list positive things you didn't quite get around to doing.

Sometimes, when you do one negative thing it leads to a long line of negative things. However, when you do one positive thing it is more powerful and spreads all around you changing your attitude, your perceptions and the way others respond to you.

Part of using this tool is to become aware of all the POSITIVE ACTIONS you take each and every day. Pay attention to your actions, and then slowly increase the number of POSITIVE ACTIONS each day.

HOW TO USE – POSITIVE ACTIONS

When you pick out two or three POSITIVE ACTIONS you will have them ready for your thought process. Having POSITIVE ACTIONS ready is important, because you may need to use them when the urge to make a poor choice seems to be pulling at you. Get your POSITIVE ACTIONS ready. Have them waiting.

Some examples of POSITIVE ACTIONS are: having a glass of water, walking around the block, exercising, picking up a good book, calling a sponsor or church friend, or cleaning up your living space.

I will choose to use Positive actions now in all My dealings. I choose Positive actions instead of negative ones. When explaining things to my children I will also use Positive actions to be an example to them.

Keith C.

One thing that I particularly like about GOGI is how the curriculum makes it abundantly clear that we all have complete control over our thoughts, choices, and actions. We and we alone choose to perceive events how ever we want, and we react to life's every day situations based on those perceptions. So what GOGI has helped me to realize is that no matter where I am or what my situation may happen to be, the outcome of my entire future rests in no one's hands but my own. My life can be as positive and as productive as I want it to be. And just that knowledge alone gives me a general sense of solace and harmony within myself. Ultimately, GOGI has given me a peace of mind and—as its name implies—a freedom from within.

Matthew B.

ACTIVITY – POSITIVE ACTIONS

In small groups have each person:

1. Pick out 2-3 POSITIVE ACTIONS that can be used any time there is the urge to do something negative.

2. Have each person keep your positive actions simple so they are easy to do, no matter where you are.

3. Have each person share their list.

Choosing your POSITIVE ACTIONS are very important, because you will do them if negative thoughts start taking up space in your mind. If it does not pass the THREE P's test, you do something else. Before you do any action ask yourself:

Is it POWERFUL?

Is it PRODUCTIVE?

Is it POSITIVE?

D. Outlaw

REVIEW – POSITIVE ACTIONS

As a tool, POSITIVE ACTIONS has you pre-select 2-3 things you can do when you get the urge to make a negative decision.

Ask yourself the THREE P's.

Is it POWERFUL?

Is it PRODUCTIVE?

Is it POSITIVE?

You can rely on your POSITIVE ACTIONS as a buffer allowing you to remain on the right course. When you get the urge to do or think something negative, you will get to your POSITIVE ACTION as quickly as possible.

Hopefully I will be attending the GOGI course this upcoming year and utilizing all the tools and techniques I learn from GOGI.
Once again thank you for your donation to the improvement of my life and my loved ones lives.

Lebert Y.

From Coach Taylor
POSITIVE ACTIONS

The GOGI TOOL called POSITIVE ACTIONS was one of the tools given to GOGI by the GOGI Girls housed in the Los Angeles County Jail in 2007. They realized that if they used POSITIVE THOUGHTS and POSITIVE WORDS, that they would naturally end up using POSITIVE ACTIONS.

Furthermore, they realized that if they had 2-3 POSITIVE ACTIONS "on hold", that they were less likely to default back to the actions that had caused them to be away from their children and families. The tool POSITIVE ACTIONS is a gift from women who wanted to return to their children and stay there.

♡ Coach

GOGI-ism

GET YOUR GOGI ON

To GET YOUR GOGI ON means you are willing to be the very best version of you. For some GOGI groups this means everything from dancing, singing, walking, talking, or simply just being of service – just GET YOUR GOGI ON!

GROUP QUESTIONS – POSITIVE ACTIONS

1. Was there a time today when you chose a POSITIVE ACTION? Please explain.
2. Was there a time today when a POSITIVE ACTION was difficult to choose? Please explain.
3. What are your favorite POSITIVE ACTIONS? Please list.
4. Do your POSITIVE ACTIONS help you overcome urges to do something negative? Please explain.
5. What can you do to choose POSITIVE ACTIONS more often each day?

GOGI-ism

TOOL TALKING

Rather than "trash" talking, the GOGI student does a lot of "Tool" Talking. Tool Talking is when two or more people are engaged in positive conversation about how they have used the GOGI TOOLS to make more positive decisions.

Thoughts from Coach Leigh Carlson

Everyday I work to only engage in POSITIVE ACTIONS and to be of service. The difference between my actions today and in my past is that I always choose an action that will improve me as a person and will serve those around me in a POWERFUL, PRODUCTIVE and POSITIVE way. Through my POSITIVE ACTIONS, I am able to consider every situation and how I act in that situation, small or large. Today, I will pick up the piece of trash instead of letting it be someone else's responsibility. Today I will smile and make eye contact instead of ignoring a man or woman on the street. Today, I will share what I have, because I can and I want to be of service. Today I will not make excuses for drinking, procrastinating, cursing, having low self-esteem, or for engaging in any negative activity. Today I choose POSITIVE ACTIONS, because POSITIVE ACTIONS keep me at my best. When I act positively, I feel positive and I am of better service to others and myself.

Recognizing the power and impact of your POSITIVE ACTIONS from right where you are is one of the most important things you can understand. No matter where you wake up, or where you call home, your POSITIVE ACTIONS improve your life, the lives of those around you, your family, and community. How can you impact anyone from jail or prison? You can reach beyond the wall to show family and community how your POSITIVE ACTIONS can make an impact and that you can give back regardless of where you are.

POSITIVE ACTIONS IN ACTION –

A young man studying with GOGI shared that it was only his choice to change his life and become involved in positive activities, focus on his education and engage in POSITIVE ACTIONS, such as joining and contributing to GOGI, that has rekindled his relationship with is mother. He had lied, cheated and stolen from her his whole life and she was finally done being hurt by his actions. After his last arrest he could not contact her, she would not respond to letters or answer his calls. It was when he took control of his life, and engaged in POSITIVE ACTIONS on a daily basis over a sustained period of time that he was able to put into POSITIVE WORDS the relationship he wanted with his mother. He was able to share his POSITIVE ACTIONS, his new way of thinking and behaving and he was even able to write to her about his new life and share his GOGI Tools. It was through consistent and positive communication that he finally, one day, received a letter from his mother. There is healing that needs to take place, but she is proud of him and he states that if it were not for his involvement with GOGI, he does not believe he would have his mother in his life, because without GOGI he was not able to take control of his situation. ***That is powerful.***

GOGI 4 Life!

Coach Carlson

Coach Carlson

WEEKLY STUDY GUIDE

(Facilitator, when possible, please make a copy of this guide and distribute at the beginning of your meeting. With this guide, students can make certain they are learning the important concepts of this week's tool)

Today's date______________________________

My name_________________________________

Please answer all questions. Please feel free to look in your book for the answers, discuss with fellow students, or ask your facilitator.

1) In what SECTION OF TOOLS does this tool belong? ______________________________

   ____

2) What MONTH OF THE YEAR is dedicated to the study of this tool? ______________________

3) What WEEKS OF THE YEAR are dedicated to the study of this tool? ______________________

   ____

4) What are the KEY WORDS for this tool?

   ____

   ____

5) What is the STATEMENT OF OWNERSHIP for this tool? ____________________

____

____

____

____

____

____

6) Think about a time in your life, either past, present, or future, when this tool might be useful to you. How might you use this tool? __________

____

____

____

____

____

____

____

____

Loren Barnhart, GOGI student, volunteer, supporter, donor, warehouse manager

GOGI Student Testimonial

I would like to say that GOGI has given me an opportunity to become a better human being with meaning, purpose, and direction. Incorporating the GOGI tools into my life has helped me over the years in countless situations. I can lead a productive life that is free from harm thanks to GOGI. Each little moment of growth overtime, has been a true miracle. After I was released, I was welcomed by amazing and wonderful people.

This has allowed me to continue my life of service and to live THE GOGI WAY. I will continue growing and experiencing positive outcomes thanks to the positive and true community that GOGI is.

GOGI 4 Life!

Volunteer Loren

SECTION THREE:

Teach Me How to GOGI TOOLS OF MOVING FORWARD

CLAIM RESPONSIBILITY
LET GO
FOR--GIVE

STATEMENT OF OWNERSHIP
CLAIM RESPONSIBILITY

CLAIM RESPONSIBILITY

From this moment forward, I CLAIM RESPONSIBILITY for all my actions and all my reactions. All my actions and my reactions today are my responsibility and I CLAIM RESPONSIBILITY.

Repeat this week's statement of ownership as often as possible. Before you get out of bed, before your meals, during a break, and before sleeping. Write this statement for added emphasis. Your weekly statement of ownership reinforces this week's tool.

MY GOGI TOOL

CLAIM RESPONSIBILITY

Weeks to study

CLAIM RESPONSIBILITY are:

3rd Week of February

3rd Week of May

3rd Week of August

3rd Week of November

KEY WORDS –
CLAIM RESPONSIBILITY

AM I PROUD OF
THIS CHOICE?

I AM RESPONSIBLE
FOR ALL MY ACTIONS
AND ALL MY REACTIONS
TODAY.

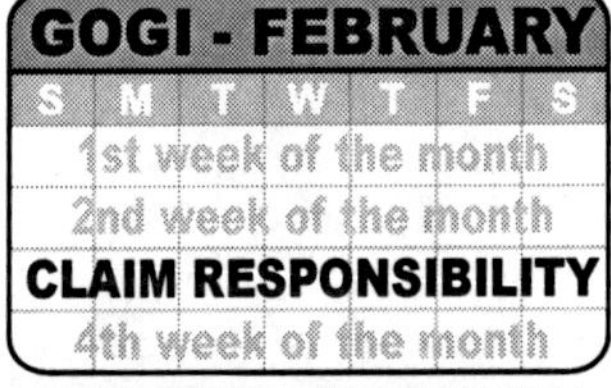

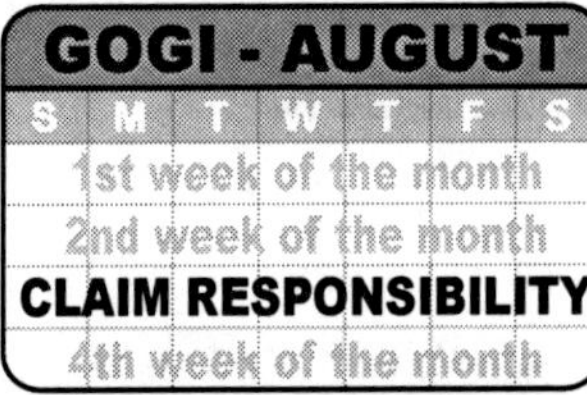

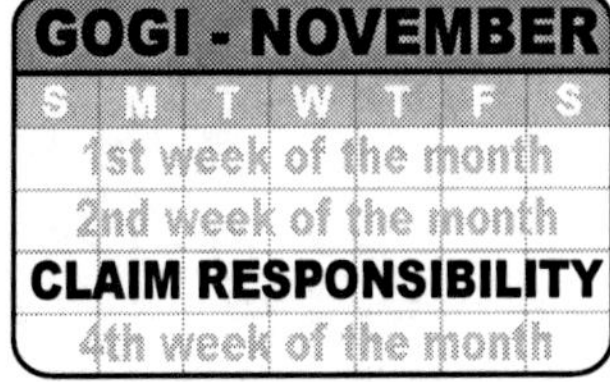

OBJECTIVE – CLAIM RESPONSIBILITY

This week you get to learn that the tool CLAIM RESPONSIBILITY puts you in charge of your reactions and actions today. CLAIM RESPONSIBILITY permits you to be the boss of how you handle problems and circumstances today.

Being Able to claim responsibility brings peace and Joy into my Life. Confronting issues without Lying gives such confidence to my soul. I feel free to face Life challenges and make decisions without thinking of past events. I no Longer feel Like the Victim I am responsible for my own actions.

Irving W.

GOGI-ism

TOOLS OF MOVING FORWARD

Students of GOGI believed that in naming this section of tools the TOOLS OF MOVING FORWARD, that other students would not get discouraged about the process of change.

CLAIM RESPONSIBILITY, LET GO and FOR — GIVE all relate to your ability to move forward into creating a more positive life for yourself.

AGENDA – CLAIM RESPONSIBILITY

Here is the outline for this week's 90-minute GOGI class/group:

1. Call Your Meeting to Order (1 min)
2. Reading of your GOGI Tools (1 min)
3. Check-in/Recap of Last Week
   A very short recap (10 mins)
4. Check GOGI national calendar
   What is the tool of this week? (1 min)
5. Reading and Activity
   For this tool from this chapter. (30 mins)
6. Group Discussions
   Found in this chapter (40-50 mins)
7. Closing Thoughts (1 min)
8. Your GOGI Pledge & Close of Meeting (5 mins)

GOGI-ism

GOGI-TUDE

This phrase was created by Peer Coach R. Rigowski. When a GOGI student shows GOGI gratitude for something positive unfolding in his life, he calls it GOGI-tude.

TOOL INTRO – CLAIM RESPONSIBILITY

CLAIM RESPONSIBILITY allows you to focus on today. You do not need to focus on yesterday and you do not need to focus on tomorrow. With CLAIM RESPONSIBILITY you focus on today.

CLAIM RESPONSIBILITY lets you be the boss of your actions and of your reactions today. How you act today and how you react today is your decision. You are the boss.

Always be proud of who you are. Hold strong to your standereds and integrity, Never live on the waves of anothers life. That is what GOGI has taught me.

I have learned and prospered from every GOGI Tool. Forgive has taught me to leave my baggage at the door and to stop the abusive Cycle in my life. Claiming Responsability has help me to be more aware of my negative patterns

Tangie R.

HOW TO USE – CLAIM RESPONSIBILITY

CLAIM RESPONSIBILITY is your power tool to help you control your actions and your reactions today. As a tool, CLAIM RESPONSIBILITY is not about the past, it is about your actions and reactions today.

You use CLAIM RESPONSIBILITY during the day when something happens or someone does something that would usually upset or concern you. With CLAIM RESPONSIBILITY you are being the boss of how you handle these situations.

Simply state: "Today I CLAIM RESPONSIBILITY for my actions and today I CLAIM RESPONSIBILITY for my reactions."

Q.8. Is GOGI-Tool-Claim Responsibility-Different-Than-as-Teacher-~~[illegible]~~ or-Parole Board Wants? And Why? or How?

A.8. Simply-Yes, it is Different. — Because,

(i) As-A-GOGI-Tool, It is a Pro-Active-Tool.

(ii) It Relates to the Future.

(iii) It Relates to the Action(s) from Present Moment/Day-Forward/Onward.

(IV.) It is Less Concerned About the Past.

(V.) It is About-Ability-to-Make-Better Choices.

(VI.) It Requires Many Things which Promote Positive Decision Making Skills

GOGI, P.O. Box 88969, LA, CA 90009-6969.

Balwinder T.

ACTIVITY – CLAIM RESPONSIBILITY

With another person or alone, list three actions or reactions today where you now CLAIM RESPONSIBILITY. These actions and reactions are not related to the past, but are related to today's challenges. State these three things aloud.

1. Can you CLAIM RESPONSIBILITY for your reactions today?
2. Can you CLAIM RESPONSIBILITY for your actions today?
3. What is the difference between reactions and actions?
4. In your group, discuss how the act of claiming responsibility is different than the GOGI TOOL called CLAIM RESPONSIBILITY.

GOGI-ism

GETTING A GOGI FIX

Many people with addiction issues want and need something positive to do and POSITIVE ACTIONS to take when old thoughts creep in. When they join or hold a GOGI Group or use their GOGI Tools to replace old thoughts and behaviors with new thoughts and behaviors they call it getting their GOGI FIX.

From Coach Taylor
CLAIM RESPONSIBILITY

As a tool, CLAIM RESPONSIBILITY is not focused on your past. As a tool, CLAIM RESPONSIBILITY works to help you not repeat the past. With this tool, you become in charge of your actions and your reactions to life's inevitable challenges. You do not fall victim to old patterns that caused you and others harm.

This tool can give you the confidence you need so that you don't need to repeat yesterday's mistakes. Rather, you now CLAIM RESPONSIBILITY for your actions and your reactions today.

What a powerful tool for you. What a wonderful way to get distance from the past and permit you to develop insight into the past. Once you use the tool CLAIM RESPONSIBILITY you can see the mistakes of the past in a different, more insightful way.

Prisoners are often stuck with a feeling that they need to CLAIM RESPONSIBILITY for their past. Sometimes this feels really impossible because of circumstances. But it is always possible to CLAIM RESPONSIBILITY for how we react today.

♡ Coach

REVIEW – CLAIM RESPONSIBILITY

As a tool, CLAIM RESPONSIBILITY is about today, not yesterday and not tomorrow. This frees you from the past long enough to create a powerful and positive today. CLAIM RESPONSIBILITY takes the pressure off the future. All you need to do with CLAIM RESPONSIBILITY is take care of your actions and your reactions today.

To use CLAIM RESPONSIBILITY simply ask yourself, "Am I proud of this choice?" Then you remind yourself that you can CLAIM RESPONSIBILITY for your actions and reactions today. Today, are you proud of this choice?

CLAIM RESPONSIBILITY is a tool that helps you make more positive choices today. If you make more positive choices today, you will be better able to repair the damage of the past. And, if you CLAIM RESPONSIBILITY for today, it is likely that tomorrow you will make more positive choices, too.

To my GOGI Family
I cant wait to take GOGI to the streets and Also to my community. I'm going to think of how to raise money to help buy books for my unfortune family members. I also want you to know I am thank full for the GOGI program, If you have anything you need help with please let me know.

Alvin B.

Thoughts from Coach Leigh Carlson

Before I make a choice everyday I ask myself, "AM I PROUD OF THIS CHOICE?" CLAIM RESPONSIBILITY is one of the most powerful tools for me personally, because it has put me in control of today and let me know that it is okay to CLAIM RESPONSIBILITY for what is good and right in my life today. CLAIM RESPONSIBILITY, as a tool, does not focus on my past.

In a lot of my struggles, personally, financially, and emotionally, I had felt like the victim. I thought I had been given a pretty raw deal. I did not CLAIM RESPONSIBILITY for how I dealt with these situations, which would have made a significant difference for me and how I allowed these situations to impact my life. Today, I can move forward with the power of CLAIM RESPONSIBILITY.

In today's world we see a lot of pointing fingers; I make sure that I look only to myself to CLAIM RESPONSIBILITY for me and I know if I AM PROUD OF THIS CHOICE, I will move beyond all my struggles.

CLAIM RESPONSIBILITY IN ACTION – At a GOGI Graduation at a Federal prison, a student came to the podium to share his thoughts on CLAIM RESPONSIBILITY. He explained that his influences in the past, his actions and decisions of the past were not going to control his decision making in the present. He had taken responsibility for his past choices and was now willing to CLAIM RESPONSIBILITY for being a better man, a man of integrity and a man that is proud of his choices today. He said that the GOGI Tool CLAIM RESPONSIBILITY enabled him to get unstuck from the past so that he could be productive in his everyday life. There was a Federal trial judge at that graduation; a man who had been on the bench for over 40 years. The judge expressed that he was excited to hear CLAIM RESPONSIBILITY redefined as such a useful and proactive tool. As a GOGI Tool, CLAIM RESPONSIBILITY can get men focused on being better today and the judge was supportive of these men. When people see the value of releasing people from the limitations of yesterday so they can improve themselves today, they can move forward with the power of CLAIM RESPONSIBILITY.

GOGI 4 Life!

Coach Leigh Carlson

GOGI-ism

GOGI Has An App for That

One GOGI student stated that his GOGI TOOLS are better than a navigational App on his phone. "Got a problem?" he said, "GOGI has an App for that."

GROUP QUESTIONS – CLAIM RESPONSIBILITY

1. Some people say it is easier to blame others and not CLAIM RESPONSIBILITY. Why?
2. Was there a time today when you used CLAIM RESPONSIBILITY as a tool to help you deal with something? Please explain.
3. Do you know anyone who uses this tool regularly? Please explain.
4. What can you do to use CLAIM RESPONSIBILITY each day?

GOGI-ism

GET GOGI WITH IT

This phrase was coined by a group of men preparing for a GOGI talent show. To GET GOGI WITH IT means you are down for living The GOGI Way and using your GOGI Tools.

WEEKLY STUDY GUIDE

(Facilitator, when possible, please make a copy of this guide and distribute at the beginning of your meeting. With this guide, students can make certain they are learning the important concepts of this week's tool)

Today's date_______________________________

My name_________________________________

Please answer all questions. Please feel free to look in your book for the answers, discuss with fellow students, or ask your facilitator.

1) In what SECTION OF TOOLS does this tool belong? ______________________________

____

2) What MONTH OF THE YEAR is dedicated to the study of this tool? ____________________

3) What WEEKS OF THE YEAR are dedicated to the study of this tool? ____________________

____

4) What are the KEY WORDS for this tool?

____

____

5) What is the STATEMENT OF OWNERSHIP for this tool? ____________________

____

____

____

____

____

____

6) Think about a time in your life, either past, present, or future, when this tool might be useful to you. How might you use this tool? __________

____

____

____

____

____

____

____

____

STATEMENT OF OWNERSHIP – LET GO

LET GO

The best way to focus on living in the present and moving forward is if I LET GO of anything which has held me back. When I LET GO, I move forward and I am setting myself free.

Repeat this week's statement of ownership as often as possible. Before you get out of bed, before your meals, during a break, and before sleeping. Write this statement for added emphasis. Your weekly statement of ownership reinforces this week's tool.

MY GOGI TOOL
LET GO

Weeks to study LET GO are:

4th Week of February

4th Week of May

4th Week of August

4th Week of November

KEY WORDS
LET GO

HAND/SQUASH/TOSS

When bothered, I put the feeling in my hand, squash it, and toss it away from me.

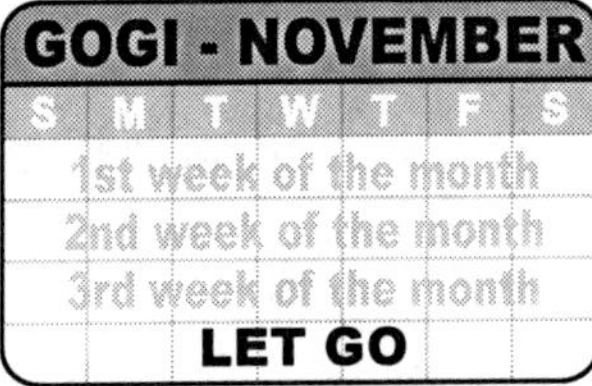

OBJECTIVE – LET GO

Your goal this week is to practice the power of putting problems in your HAND, then SQUASHING them and TOSSING them away. This tool, called LET GO, will permit you to HAND/ SQUASH/TOSS anything that might stand in your way of change.

My entire life, I've been reluctant to let things go, for fear of being regarded as a pushover, or weak, Especially when you take into consideration that I'm only 5 feet 3 inches tall. I believed the anger, and stories of disappointment would somehow "Add" to my height. I was wrong. Being able to Let Go! has removed the weight that was keeping me down and now there is nothing stopping me from growing to my full potential with G.O.G.I.

Kevin O.

AGENDA – LET GO

Here is the outline for this week's 90-minute GOGI class/group:

1. Call Your Meeting to Order (1 min)
2. Reading of your GOGI Tools (1 min)
3. Check-in/Recap of Last Week
   A very short recap (10 mins)
4. Check GOGI national calendar
   What is the tool of this week? (1 min)
5. Reading and Activity
   For this tool from this chapter. (30 mins)
6. Group Discussions
   Found in this chapter (40-50 mins)
7. Closing Thoughts (1 min)
8. Your GOGI Pledge & Close of Meeting (5 mins)

This tool works volumes when you use it right. It's a stress reliever, helps you cope with issues past, present & future. Helps you walk through the issues until you reach the big ones.

Matthew D.

TOOL INTRO – LET GO

GOGI knows there are things in your past that might seem too big to ever move beyond. Sometimes it seems as if the bad stuff has controlled and defined your life. That is sometimes a normal way to feel.

You can use the GOGI TOOL called LET GO for the big things, but also for the daily little things. You can begin to use this tool to get past the daily irritations that happen to everyone.

Let Go / Hand / Squash / Toss

Let go is a beautiful tool. Even though it can be challenging for some to use, once its put to practice and perfected. Let Go can be used to defuse anything that might irritate or agitate you.
To be able to rid yourself of everyday stress or pain by using three jesters. My hand, to put bad thoughts and feelings in, then Squash, to get it out of my body and mind, to Toss It, like a puff of smoke into the air. Having fun while getting rid of the problems that are holding you back. I could do that. By Letting Go, I can make a big change in my life. Starting with the small stuff, working my way to the Big Stuff.

Matthew L.

HOW TO USE – TOOL LET GO

You use LET GO for the daily irritations, those things that seem to creep up on you and try to trip you up.

Someone bumps into you? Give it the LET GO - HAND/SQUASH/TOSS and LET GO. Didn't get that job? Give it the LET GO. Didn't like how someone spoke to you? Give it the LET GO.

The more you use LET GO for the little daily things, the more powerfully it can help you with those old things that might still be bothering you.

It's easier for me when I use this tool for little things. For example, today someone cursed me out because he thought I said something bad to him. I know I didn't say anything to him or anybody at all. I decided to not say anything back to him or react negatively towards him.

Jose R.

GOGI-ism

THE GOGI GLOW

When women completed the GOGI Group study and were awarded certificates of completion from their facility, one woman stated that they appeared to have THE GOGI GLOW on their faces!

ACTIVITY – LET GO

In small groups or working alone, you will find this activity is freeing and fun.

1. Think of something that bothers you. If you like, you can write this down on a piece of paper.
2. Put this thing in your hand, or imagine it in the palm of your hand.
3. Go ahead and squash it. Crumple up all the emotion around this thing.

We call this HAND, SQUASH, TOSS. Put it in your HAND, then SQUASH and TOSS it. If your group wants, you can put everyone's squashables in one big pile, or put them all in a trash can so everyone can be free together.

I was up at night and couldn't sleep I had to many negative thoughts flowing one after another bigger and worst than each other I thought about this last step Let go we just went over I stuck my hands in the air and as the thought came I just closed my hand tight and flung it towards the outside window and thought about something new then the next one came and I repeated the whole act again it felt good and I've been doing this everytime I get a negative thought I crush it and toss it far from me

Dorian A.

REVIEW – LET GO

LET GO is liberating, because it gets all the emotion and irritation out of your body and into your hand for you to do the LET GO - HAND/SQUASH/TOSS.

When you LET GO, there is more room in your body for positive decisions. You will not be controlled by others or by situations if you LET GO. If you LET GO, you are being the boss. You are in control of your responses. You are in control of your reactions.

Just remember, LET GO is all about the HAND/SQUASH/TOSS and you can do it a million times a day, if you like.

GOGI-ism

YOUR GOGI GAME CHANGER

One of the Salt Lake County GOGI Peer Coaches, Tevita, asked his students this question. It became a regular question asked in many GOGI Groups. He asked, "When it came to GOGI, what was the GAME CHANGER tool? What GOGI Tool, what moment, what happened that made you say – this is it – I AM GOGI 4 LIFE!" What is your GOGI GAME CHANGER?

From Coach Taylor
LET GO

The LET GO tool was designed by women who felt LET GO was a good tool to help with every day frustrations. Then the men gave it the action of putting it in your HAND, SQUASHING it and TOSSING it. For both men and women, and even kids, this is a real easy way to get rid of overwhelming urges or emotions.

LET GO is a great tool to immediately let you regain your power. Sometimes emotions feel as if they flood your body and force you into an action you later regret.

LET GO is perfect for this because it puts you in the place of power where you can get that problem or situation in your hand, you squash it, and toss it. You do not let your future success be distracted by anything that might trip you up when you use your tool, LET GO. You LET GO and get going toward your planned destination.

♡ Coach

GROUP QUESTIONS – LET GO

1. What is one thing that happened today, when you could use the tool LET GO and do your HAND/SQUASH/TOSS?

2. Is there something coming up in the future where LET GO and the HAND/SQUASH/TOSS will be helpful? Please explain.

3. What are some of the small daily irritants where LET GO will work?

4. What are some of the bigger challenges in using LET GO?

Yesi Amaya

Thoughts from Coach Leigh Carlson

Before I had the GOGI Tool LET GO in my toolbox, I was plagued by anxiety and let daily stress get the best of me. The kicker is that none, not one of the things that caused me so much stress, was within my control. The only thing in my control was how I handled these situations. I had to LET GO to get beyond these situations. LET GO has freed me from years of unnecessary anxiety and poor decisions. When I LET GO of the little things each day, I am not bottling up the worry and irritation so that it can get the best of me and I will not wallow in a negative situation.

I have the GOGI TOOLS posted right next to my desk at work, along with a sign that says, "LET GO". I can often be found at my desk doing the HAND/SQUASH/TOSS. I might look funny, but I feel amazing. No matter what your style of LET GO, you can march to the beat of your own drummer, as long as you LET GO - HAND/SQUASH/TOSS. Don't carry it around with you if you can get it out of your system and move on to processing bigger and more important things. LET GO.

People have a difficult time with LET GO, especially when they identify strongly with something - good or bad. You have a place in life and a reputation and you identify with that, but perhaps your identity is not healthy; perhaps your lifestyle is destructive, and perhaps you are in prison or jail because you have made decisions that are not your best, because, you have allowed your label to dictate your life. How can you simply LET GO of your identity or label without losing yourself? LET

GO requires you to identify with something else, something different, and for you to pick your own labels. LET GO is not about not being who you are, it is about showing up differently in the world; showing up in a productive and positive way. Here is an example.

LET GO IN ACTION –

A young man is sentenced to life at the age of 16 for second-degree murder. In his city real men carry guns, respect is earned through violence, and real men go to prison. He saw that his whole life, heard that his whole life and was told his whole life that he would end up just like his father – in prison. And so he did. This young man identified so much with what he was told he was, that he did not even see an alternative. He took on that label, and with no other information he wore that label straight to prison on a life term. Today that man is 42 years old. He is not the boy he was 25 years ago; he is a grown man who has LET GO of those old destructive beliefs; he is a grown man that does not identify with violence and anger. He is now a GOGI Peer Coach. He is now a college student. He is now a good father, brother, uncle and mentor. He is now what he chooses to be. He took the long lonely journey away from the familiar. He LET GO of what everyone told him he was and what he identified as for so long and he paved his own way. It was not easy, but his life has taken on new meaning and he lives today as an example for good. If it does not serve you today, LET GO.

GOGI 4 Life!

Coach Carlson

Coach Carlson

WEEKLY STUDY GUIDE

(Facilitator, when possible, please make a copy of this guide and distribute at the beginning of your meeting. With this guide, students can make certain they are learning the important concepts of this week's tool)

Today's date______________________________

My name________________________________

Please answer all questions. Please feel free to look in your book for the answers, discuss with fellow students, or ask your facilitator.

1) In what SECTION OF TOOLS does this tool belong? ______________________________

   ____

2) What MONTH OF THE YEAR is dedicated to the study of this tool? ____________________

3) What WEEKS OF THE YEAR are dedicated to the study of this tool? ____________________

   ____

4) What are the KEY WORDS for this tool?

   ____

   ____

5) What is the STATEMENT OF OWNERSHIP for this tool? ________________________________

____

____

____

____

____

____

6) Think about a time in your life, either past, present, or future, when this tool might be useful to you. How might you use this tool? __________

____

____

____

____

____

____

____

____

STATEMENT OF OWNERSHIP
FOR--GIVE

FOR--GIVE

FOR me to GIVE back to others I make sure I am safe from harm. FOR me to GIVE, I make sure I am safe.

Repeat this week's statement of ownership as often as possible. Before you get out of bed, before your meals, during a break, and before sleeping. Write this statement for added emphasis. Your weekly statement of ownership reinforces this week's tool.

MY GOGI TOOL
FOR--GIVE

Weeks to study FOR--GIVE are:

1st Week of March

1st Week of June

1st Week of September

1st Week of December

KEY WORDS
FOR--GIVE

FOR ME TO GIVE,
I NEED DISTANCE
FROM HARM.

For me to give, I unhook from the past, and find my internal freedom.

GOGI - MARCH
S M T W T F S
FOR--GIVE (or FOR-GIVING)
2nd week of the month
3rd week of the month
4th week of the month

GOGI - JUNE
S M T W T F S
FOR--GIVE (or FOR-GIVING)
2nd week of the month
3rd week of the month
4th week of the month

GOGI - SEPTEMBER
S M T W T F S
FOR--GIVE (or FOR-GIVING)
2nd week of the month
3rd week of the month
4th week of the month

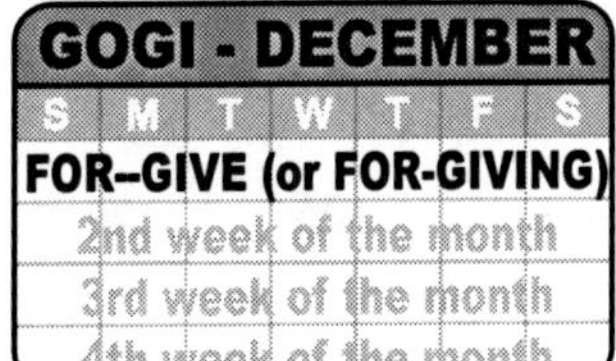

OBJECTIVE – FOR--GIVE

This week you get to practice being the boss of how much past harm and past hurt you carry with you. You get to focus on being safe from more harm so that you can GIVE back to others and make your world a better place. FOR you to GIVE, you will learn to keep yourself safe.

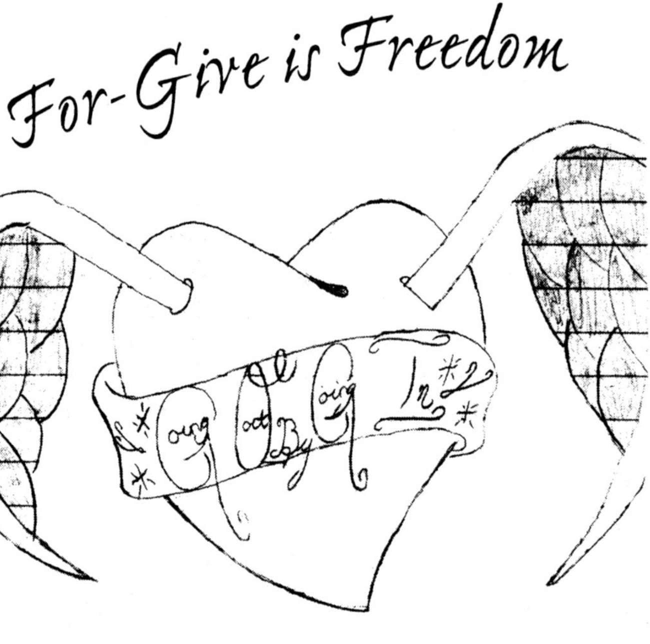

For-Give is Freedom

Joshua W.

AGENDA – FOR--GIVE

Here is the outline for this week's 90-minute GOGI class/group:

1. Call Your Meeting to Order (1 min)
2. Reading of your GOGI Tools (1 min)
3. Check-in/Recap of Last Week
   A very short recap (10 mins)
4. Check GOGI national calendar
   What is the tool of this week? (1 min)
5. Reading and Activity
   For this tool from this chapter (30 mins)
6. Group Discussions
   Found in this chapter (40-50 mins)
7. Closing Thoughts (1 min)
8. Your GOGI Pledge & Close of Meeting (5 mins)

Poem by GOGI student Ryan N.

It took 3Ps to be the BOSS OF MY BRAIN.
It took the SMART PART, to begin my claim to
LET GO of all my shame.
It took the EMOTIONAL PART to start to FOR--GIVE.
To a REALITY CHECK of WHAT IF. WHAT IF I took an
old habit and let a new action in.
It took BELLY BREATHING to start to begin, to slow me
down and put on a positive spin.
Cuz POSITIVE THOUGHTS lead to POSITIVE WORDS and
that's where ULTIMATE FREEDOM and POSITIVE starts.
And that's how I'm Getting Out by Going In.

TOOL INTRO – FOR--GIVE

For you to be really happy, you will eventually discover that you need to give your time and energy to others to help them. This is how lasting happiness is created. But FOR you to GIVE, you need to get yourself safe from harm. FOR you to be a GIVING individual, you must be getting distance from addiction or abuse. You must be SAFE ENOUGH TO GIVE.

FOR--GIVE as a GOGI TOOL requires that you get yourself in a safe enough position so you can begin to give back to others.

I think anyone can FOR-GIVE and find safety. I believe you have to know about yourself first and have some stability in your life. Once you are recovered from all your bad habits and addiction then you can help others figure out how to overcome whatever it is that is setting them back.

Tony U.

HOW TO USE – FOR--GIVE

As a tool, FOR--GIVE is about being safe enough for you to give back. This means if the harm is really close, you need to get to safety. If your addiction is the harm, you need to get to the safety offered by programs, churches, sober societies, and other support systems.

You need to be a sufficient distance from the harm–causing person or circumstance. It is nearly impossible to forgive when the danger is right there in front of you. In fact, it is not wise to place an alcoholic in a bar, an addict next to a needle, or a thief next to unguarded jewels. FOR--GIVE is about protection. Make sure you and everyone around you is safe enough FOR you to GIVE back and FOR you to be the GIVING person you were meant to be.

Moving forward helps me "forgive" myself of my Past

ACTIVITY – FOR--GIVE

In small groups, in pairs, or by yourself, this activity will help you discover how to make sure you are safe enough to start giving back to others.

1. Share one thing that is difficult for you to forgive. This could be a lie, being stolen from, or it could be a bigger thing that is difficult for you to forgive. It could be something you have done.
2. Share with the group if you are still in danger of having this thing happen to you again.
3. Discuss with your group what you think it would take for you to be safe enough FOR you to GIVE and FOR you to start GIVING back to others.
4. FOR you to GIVE, share with the group what you will do today or tomorrow that gives back to others.

GOGI-ism

A GOGI OUT

Guys in New York City were engaged in GOGI Group study, but after group some of the men returned to their arguing and trash-talking. One of the leaders suggested that to break the old habit of the way they treated each other, all the person had to say was "I am taking a GOGI OUT." This is the permission to walk away from any potential altercation. For them, a GOGI OUT was more powerful than remaining in the conflict.

REVIEW – FOR--GIVE

FOR--GIVE is about safety and getting yourself far enough from the harm FOR you to start GIVING back to others. You can't really be of service to others when you are dodging danger or when you are afraid of being victimized again. Safety is a critical part of you being in charge of your life. And, once you are safe, you can use FOR--GIVE to start GIVING back and being the best version of you.

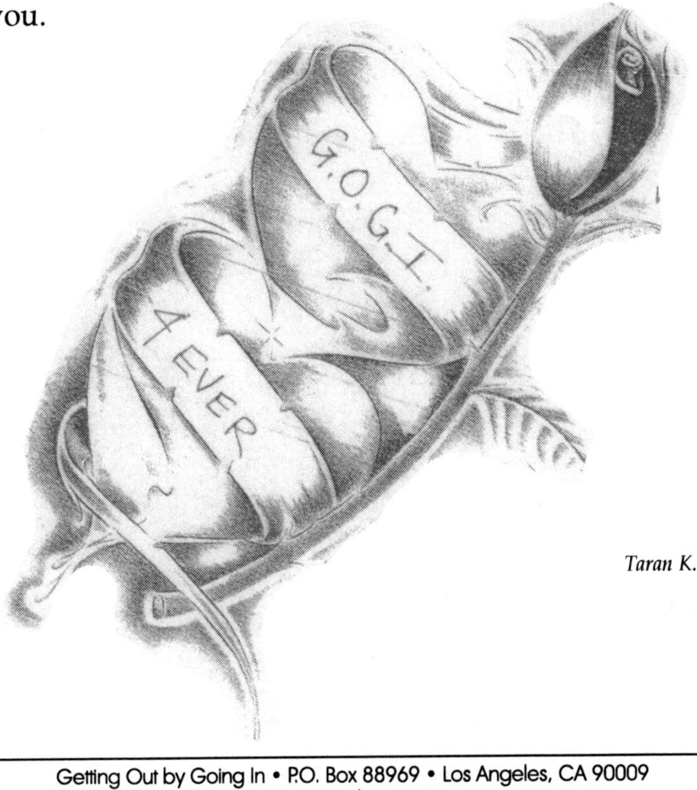

Taran K.

From Coach Taylor
FOR--GIVE

Many GOGI students had a challenge in thinking of FOR--GIVE as a tool. They got it confused with the act of forgiving. But the two are very different. As a tool, FOR--GIVE is about you creating the safety FOR you to GIVE back. The funny thing is, when you start to give back, you find that forgiving comes naturally. Why? Because you have created safety from future harm.

FOR--GIVE is about being safe enough for you to give back to others. This tool was clarified by men who stated that it was easy for them to forgive others when they were in service, but it was difficult to be in service when they were fighting addiction or harm. FOR them to GIVE they needed distance from the harm.

If you are struggling with the harm you experienced or the harm you caused others and you are finding it difficult to forgive, then the tool FOR--GIVE is perfect. You make sure you are a safe distance from harm. Get distance from your own behavior. Get distance from those who hurt you. Get distance and THEN begin to give of yourself to others. FOR--GIVE is all about you getting to a safe place so you can give.

♡ Coach

Thoughts from Coach Leigh Carlson

With the GOGI Tool FOR--GIVE, for the first time in my life, I was able to GIVE back to a friend struggling with addiction. This was possible because I had separated myself enough from my old negative habits, situations and people to know that I would never engage in that behavior again. Because I was safe and confident in my ability not to harm myself or be harmed by others through poor decision-making, I was then able to help someone I love cope with his battle with addiction. I was able to forgive myself for all of the bad decisions I had made and forgive others for harm they caused me as a result of unhealthy relationships. I was able to GIVE back in a meaningful way, because his struggles were similar to mine. There is a world full of people who can use your guidance because you have lived it, you know it, and there is no better inspiration or example, and no better way to GIVE back than through your experiences. FOR--GIVE as a tool means that if I protect myself from harm, there will be no stronger advocate FOR-GIVING back in a powerful and meaningful way.

FOR--GIVE IN ACTION –

GOGI received a letter from a prisoner in the Secure Housing Unit of a Federal prison. He found a GOGI book and was studying on his

GOGI-ism

To GOGI UP

Like the term "word up", to GOGI UP means you are willing to create your life from this day forward using your GOGI TOOLS. You are willing to GOGI UP.

own. He mentioned that he was excited about GOGI. He said that it challenged the way he had been thinking and acting his entire life. He had finally found something positive to commit to after a life committed to criminal behavior. Although his communication was limited with others, he was always sharing the tools with his cellie, the other men in SHU and with the officers whenever possible. He would share in anyway he could as he prepared for transfer. He stated that he wanted teach GOGI in SHU, but it was tough, therefore he simply shared as well as he could. And he made a promise to himself and GOGI that when he arrived at his new location, he would start a GOGI Group there.

This man separated himself from the violence and damage of his previous life enough to see that he could GIVE back to others. He was safe from that old decision-making and he trusted that he did not need to engage in that lifestyle. He was safe enough to give back through his experiences. The prison he transferred to now has several active GOGI Groups facilitated by GOGI students, recognized by the facility and supported by staff. He is actively facilitating GOGI Groups. FOR—GIVE in action indeed!

GOGI 4 Life!

Coach Carlson

Coach Carlson

GROUP QUESTIONS – FOR--GIVE

1. Why do you think safety is so important FOR you to GIVE back?
2. Does focusing on your safety make you think of the words forgiveness and forgive in a different way? Please explain.
3. How is the tool FOR--GIVE different from the action forgive?
4. Can everyone find safety? Can everyone FOR--GIVE? Please explain.

When we use GOGI FOR-GIVE we are actually giving back something in return. It takes us forward and stops our recurring pain. We learn to distance our self from the potential harm. And then we learn to squash that harm we carried with us for so long.

Yen C.

WEEKLY STUDY GUIDE

(Facilitator, when possible, please make a copy of this guide and distribute at the beginning of your meeting. With this guide, students can make certain they are learning the important concepts of this week's tool)

Today's date________________________________

My name__________________________________

Please answer all questions. Please feel free to look in your book for the answers, discuss with fellow students, or ask your facilitator.

1) In what SECTION OF TOOLS does this tool belong? ______________________________

   ____

2) What MONTH OF THE YEAR is dedicated to the study of this tool? __________________

3) What WEEKS OF THE YEAR are dedicated to the study of this tool? __________________

   ____

4) What are the KEY WORDS for this tool?

   ____

   ____

5) What is the STATEMENT OF OWNERSHIP for this tool? ______________________________

____

____

____

____

____

____

6) Think about a time in your life, either past, present, or future, when this tool might be useful to you. How might you use this tool? __________

____

____

____

____

____

____

____

____

Anthony Michael Jefferson
GOGI champion, volunteer, advocate

TESTIMONIAL

What is the boisterous sound welling up inside of me compelling me to move forward. GOGI whisperings, CLAIM RESPONSIBILITY - LET GO – FOR--GIVE with each passing second, moment and hour of the internal clock. My breath deepens, my mind expands and I envision walking over and turning on the LIGHTSWITCH of my new perception. GOGI whisperings. I am the BOSS OF MY BRAIN. Decisions – decisions, choices to be made. POSITIVE THOUGHTS – WORDS – ACTIONS with them a new reality has thus been paved. I am, we are POSITIVE – PRODUCTIVE – POWERFUL in this dawn of a new day, a new way of being, seeing inside. My thoughts, my choices, my ability to move forward have given me the tools of creation. WHAT IF I healthily examine my past and its painful realities, that my new principles come before personalities. WHAT IF I am willing to delay instant gratification and do away with my compulsion? My core of light, divine intelligence creates a new reality. Checking in with myself, I have taken ten steps forward, taken two steps back. I know the science of my mind has me eight steps ahead and that's infinitely divine. ULTIMATE FREEDOM has blossomed within the reflection so simple. I look into the stilled waters again. The new me radiant. Forgiving, powerful and productive. Getting Out by Going In allows me to serve others willingly, joyfully, and unconditionally. Seeing their potential seeing the tapestry of We, WHO ARE WE? WE ARE GOGI!

GOGI Graduate
Anthony Michael Jefferson

SECTION FOUR:

Teach Me How to GOGI

TOOLS OF CREATION

WHAT IF

REALITY CHECK

ULTIMATE FREEDOM

STATEMENT OF OWNERSHIP
WHAT IF

WHAT IF

WHAT IF permits me to see possibilities I might not otherwise realize. Today, I ask myself, WHAT IF I am not my past? WHAT IF I reached my goal? WHAT IF I actually improved my life today, tomorrow and the next day?

Repeat this week's statement of ownership as often as possible. Before you get out of bed, before your meals, during a break, and before sleeping. Write this statement for added emphasis. Your weekly statement of ownership reinforces this week's tool.

MY GOGI TOOL
WHAT IF

Weeks to study WHAT IF are:

2nd Week of March

2nd Week of June

2nd Week of September

2nd Week of December

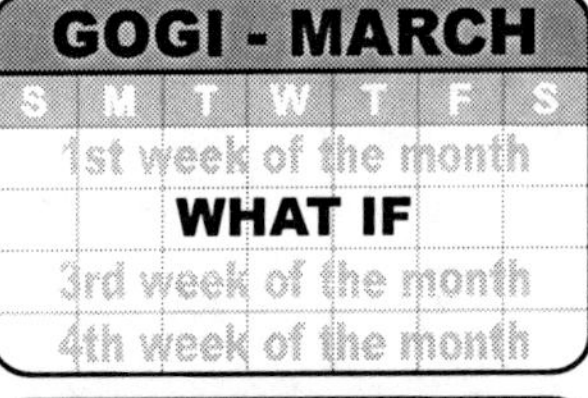

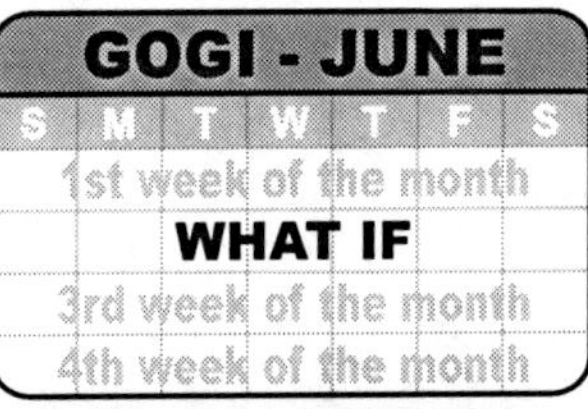

KEY WORDS
WHAT IF

WHAT IF I AM NOT MY PAST?

No to the past = yes to the future.

OBJECTIVE – WHAT IF

Your goal this week is to be the boss of your future. You do this by asking the WHAT IF question, because when you look at the possible outcome for the future you will make better decisions in the present. WHAT IF is the tool you can use to build your positive future.

Daily living in prison begins with the desire for ULTIMATE FREEDOM. Just BEING FREE IS UP TO ME. This is the true REALITY CHECK, being able to understand the TEN AND TWO RULE. Is it safe to say no to the past and yes to the future? The questions is WHAT IF? Is it safe to give? I need to unhook from the past and FOR--GIVE, LET GO, it is as easy as using HAND/SQUASH/TOSS. Life is all about the tool of CLAIM RESPONSIBILITY, I will own today" and I am proud of this choice. I will continue from this point to be POWERFUL, PRODUCTIVE and POSITIVE by displaying POSITIVE ACTIONS in my control, POSITIVE WORDS in what I say, and always trying to use POSITIVE THOUGHTS. The key will be to use the FIVE SECOND LIGHTSWITCH, releasing old thoughts and creating new positive thoughts, feeling the flow through my daily BELLY BREATHING and embracing the principal that I am BOSS OF MY BRAIN.

Francis C.

AGENDA – WHAT IF

Here is the outline for this week's 90-minute GOGI class/group:

1. Call Your Meeting to Order (1 min)
2. Reading of your GOGI Tools (1 min)
3. Check-in/Recap of Last Week
   A very short recap (10 mins)
4. Check GOGI national calendar
   What is the tool of this week? (1 min)
5. Reading and Activity
   For this tool from this chapter (30 mins)
6. Group Discussions
   Found in this chapter (40-50 mins)
7. Closing Thoughts (1 min)
8. Your GOGI Pledge & Close of Meeting (5 mins)

WHAT IF I just LET GO, think positive, talk about POSITIVE ACTIONS, take five seconds to recall BOSS OF MY BRAIN, CLAIM RESPONSIBILITY for my reactions. REALITY CHECK defined perfectly. FOR--GIVE to remember God's blessing is to be of service leading to ULTIMATE FREEDOM. Thank you GOGI.

Peer Coach Eugene C.

TOOL INTRO – WHAT IF

The tool WHAT IF is really cool because it gives you a glimpse into what might be possible.

You can use WHAT IF for the negative to avoid negative outcomes. You can also use WHAT IF for the positive, to see new positive possibilities.

WHAT IF is your ability to look into the future and see the likely outcome of any action you take.

With this ability, you can set goals for yourself and clearly see the benefit of working toward a positive outcome. WHAT IF you are not your past?

This critical question frees you to become a benefit to society because of your past! WHAT IF you are needed as the solution?

GOGI-ism

TOOLS OF CREATION

When you understand the power of WHAT IF, REALITY CHECK and ULTIMATE FREEDOM, you are creating the most powerful life possible. GOGI students named this section of tools the TOOLS OF CREATION as a result of that power you now have over how you respond to life's inevitable challenges.

HOW TO USE – WHAT IF

You can use the GOGI Tool WHAT IF for everything you do during the day. WHAT IF you wake up early? WHAT IF you don't? WHAT IF you go to that meeting? WHAT IF you don't?

WHAT IF places you in charge, because you are choosing every minute of the day what you want to endorse in your life. You are checking out the possible outcomes with the WHAT IF tool and you are clearly stating the direction of your life from now onward.

WHAT IF can permit you a glimpse into the future. You can say "WHAT IF I don't go to a meeting and I start thinking about drinking?" And you can also say, "WHAT IF I do go to a meeting and I am able to sit with other people who are on a positive path?"

WHAT IF gives you a snapshot of what is likely to happen with your decision.

What if helped me to stop and consider what my outcomes will be to my actions. What if is a tool that makes you play out the negative and positive outcomes of the situation before it happens and lets you know or lets you realize what can happen. This tool helps you overcome the wave of emotions that blocks your ability to make positive decisions.

Joshua M.

ACTIVITY – WHAT IF

In groups or alone, this activity will be interesting, because it will allow you to see new possibilities for yourself and others.

1. One person at a time, state a positive WHAT IF. As an example, "WHAT IF I drink water instead of beer for the rest of my life? " or "WHAT IF I go back to school and graduate?"
2. The group responds with possible outcomes. As an example, "Then you would remain sober and not struggle so much."
3. Repeat this until each group member is able to state 3-4 of their WHAT IFs and permit the group to respond with the positive outcomes.

Here is another WHAT IF activity

1. Write down several WHAT IF situations on pieces of paper. Mix the pieces of paper together.
2. Have each group member pull a piece of paper and read it.
3. Each member then projects the likely outcome of that WHAT IF.

From Coach Taylor
WHAT IF

WHAT IF was designed by women who suffered from low self-esteem. They didn't know it was possible to build self esteem by making positive choices. One woman asked me, "Coach Taylor, WHAT IF I am not my past?" That is how the tool WHAT IF was added to the GOGI tool box.

♡ Coach

Let-Go is the one that helps you inside — To SQUASH it IN YOUR HAND and TOSS IT TO THE SIDE.

Forgive - alone the word seems real nice but getting away is the best advice!
To be safe from harm seems TO WORK BEST
Keep it in mind and you'll pass all your TEST.
NOW WHAT-IF is Great in everything you do. Because WHAT-IF YOU DO! You'll END UP IN SHU ⍨
Reality Check is the walk we all take!
10 steps forward till we make a mistake
1 or 2 backwards it won't hurt that much
Your still ahead 8 now that is good luck.
WHOA ULTIMATE FREEDOM We've all done that here, whether it's an envelope, stamp or even a chair. The women in here are generous you see LET'S PRAY the use the GOGI Tools once there SET FREE!

Utah State Prison, Women

REVIEW – WHAT IF

WHAT IF is your way to see the likely outcome of any situation. With WHAT IF you can see what will happen if you drink or get angry, because you can play out your own actions and reactions, as well as other people's reactions to your choices.

With WHAT IF, you can also see what might happen when your choices are positive. You can see what will happen if you eat healthy, drink more water, walk more, attend more positive meetings. With WHAT IF, you can see the positive side of putting down the cigarette and walking around the block.

WHAT IF is like being the director of your very own movie. You create every scene by your choices and how you choose to respond to others in your movie.

WHAT IF? is very powerful. This is the primary method I use to stay on course and achieve my goals. When there is potential for a negative outcome, I play it through so I can see the consequences. I then play it through toward a positive outcome so I can see the positive side. By going through this process, I am able to make a clear decision with a high degree of certainty of the outcome.

Harold H.

Thoughts from Coach Leigh Carlson

The GOGI Tool WHAT IF has my back, because it gives me options. WHAT IF reminds me that I can create an amazing future, that I have choices, and I am going to make them positive. Years ago when I did not have my GOGI Tools, many of the obstacles I faced daily would impede my progress and cause me great anxiety. Today, with my GOGI TOOLS, I can ask myself WHAT IF I view this obstacle differently? WHAT IF this obstacle exists because I stand to learn a great deal by overcoming this challenge?

We have all been down the negative road, down the list of negative WHAT IFs, and we all know what that thought process can do to us. WHAT IF gives me permission to imagine the possibilities, and when I look forward to the positive WHAT IFs, I find that I work towards them as well. It is not about predicting the future; it is about playing an active role in the positive possibilities of your future.

WHAT IF IN ACTION – *There is a man I like to call Mr. WHAT IF. He is a man who does not limit himself or his goals and always thinks through his WHAT Ifs. WHAT IF I go left? WHAT if I go right? He gauges all choices with WHAT IF, but he also is willing to see through a lens of possibility. He no longer says, WHAT IF I fail? He says WHAT IF I succeed? WHAT IF I am wrong? Is now WHAT IF I am right? WHAT IF is no limits. WHAT IF is, if you want it, work towards it; WHAT IF lets you write the script, lets you turn the page and say - in this chapter my life gets better.*

Mr. WHAT IF is in prison. He asks himself, WHAT IF I am here, because it is my duty to share with others what has been shared with me. WHAT IF I am right where I am, because there is someone that needs my guidance? WHAT IF I need their guidance? WHAT IF? He says WHAT IF I live my life in such a way that no one can deny that I have transformed inside and out. WHAT IF I live this way regardless of the outcome? WHAT IF I am here all my life? I will be a good and productive man in here. WHAT IF I get released? I will be a good and productive man out there. WHAT IF I am a good and productive man? WHAT IF no one can take that from me? WHAT IF?

GOGI 4 Life!

Coach Carlson

GOGI Girls of Dublin

GROUP QUESTIONS – WHAT IF

1. How is WHAT IF a good tool to realize the outcome of actions?
2. How can WHAT IF help you plan for your future?
3. How can WHAT IF keep you from making negative decisions?
4. Does WHAT IF help people with addictions? How?
5. Do you think WHAT IF would be a good tool to teach children? Why?

WEEKLY STUDY GUIDE

(Facilitator, when possible, please make a copy of this guide and distribute at the beginning of your meeting. With this guide, students can make certain they are learning the important concepts of this week's tool)

Today's date________________________________

My name___________________________________

Please answer all questions. Please feel free to look in your book for the answers, discuss with fellow students, or ask your facilitator.

1) In what SECTION OF TOOLS does this tool belong? ______________________________

   ____

2) What MONTH OF THE YEAR is dedicated to the study of this tool? ______________________

3) What WEEKS OF THE YEAR are dedicated to the study of this tool? ______________________

   ____

4) What are the KEY WORDS for this tool?

   ____

   ____

5) What is the STATEMENT OF OWNERSHIP for this tool? ______________________________

____

____

____

____

____

____

6) Think about a time in your life, either past, present, or future, when this tool might be useful to you. How might you use this tool? __________

____

____

____

____

____

____

____

____

STATEMENT OF OWNERSHIP
REALITY CHECK

REALITY CHECK

I know I am going to make mistakes along the way, but REALITY CHECK lets me quickly correct my mistakes. Today, I agree to get right back on track with REALITY CHECK when I do something that is not perfect.

Repeat this week's statement of ownership as often as possible. Before you get out of bed, before your meals, during a break, and before sleeping. Write this statement for added emphasis. Your weekly statement of ownership reinforces this week's tool.

MY GOGI TOOL
REALITY CHECK

Weeks to study REALITY CHECK are:

3rd Week of March

3rd Week of June

3rd Week of September

3rd Week of December

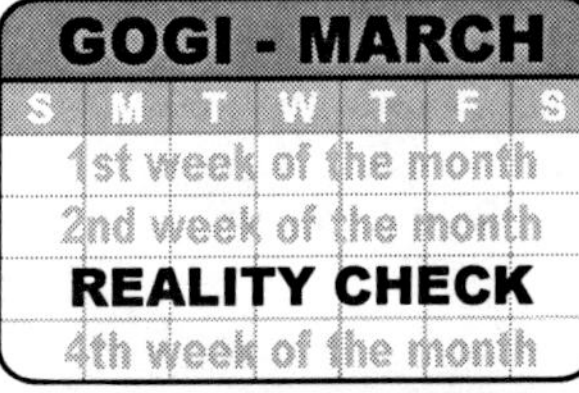

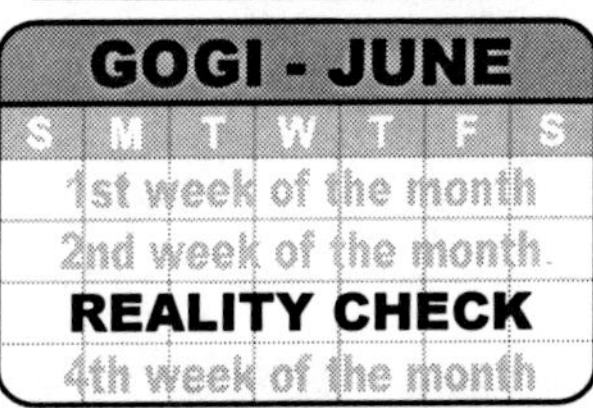

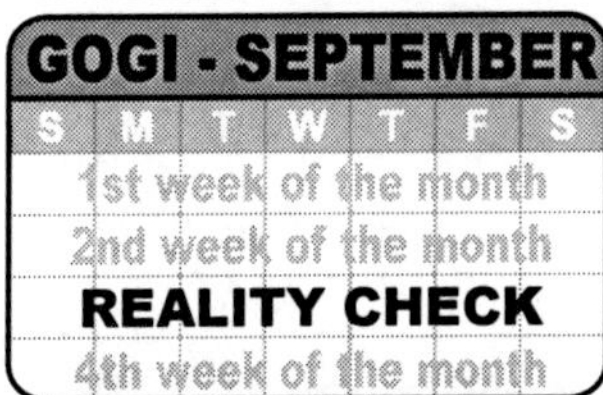

KEY WORDS
REALITY CHECK

TEN AND TWO RULE

Ten steps forward and two steps back is still eight steps ahead.

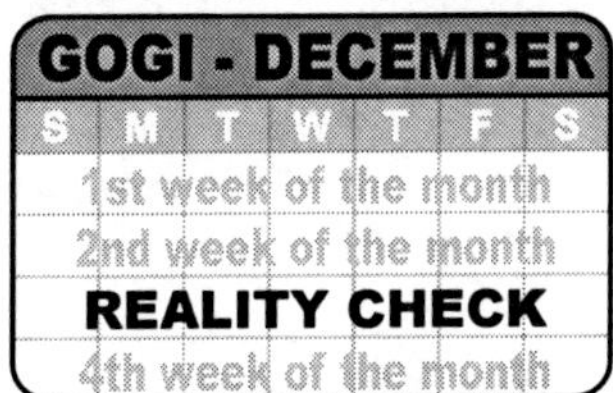

OBJECTIVE – REALITY CHECK

Your goal this week is to realize that you are human and you will make mistakes, but that does not mean you are not successful. This week's tool, REALITY CHECK, permits you to be the boss and recover from bad decisions quickly.

I really don't know how to describe how valuable the 12 tools of GOGI have been in my life, other than if it weren't for GOGI, the wonderful staff at GOGI, and most importantly the 12 tools of GOGI, I would not have a life! GOGI has shown me that there is another path to go down, a more positive less self-destructive path. Can it be hard sometimes? Yes! It can be very hard sometimes. But, something that I have learned while studying GOGI and trying to better myself is that nothing worth having in life is easy. If it were easy and worth having, everyone would have it. We all know that's not the case! So GOGI has really given me something to live for in a place where most people want to give up.

Peer Coach Trevor L.

AGENDA – REALITY CHECK

Here is the outline for this week's 90-minute GOGI class/group:

1. Call Your Meeting to Order (1 min)
2. Reading of your GOGI Tools (1 min)
3. Check-in/Recap of Last Week
   A very short recap (10 mins)
4. Check GOGI national calendar
   What is the tool of this week? (1 min)
5. Reading and Activity
   For this tool from this chapter (30 mins)
6. Group Discussions
   Found in this chapter (40-50 mins)
7. Closing Thoughts (1 min)
8. Your GOGI Pledge & Close of Meeting (5 mins)

It was so cool, But the Distric Prosacutter D.A. came to me and ask If I was still doing GOGI? Yes I said, It has changed my Life, He stated he believed that and that he wanted to thank me for Pushing to Get it Started at Heker for the men he is seeing a differance in the men! (Wow)

Wesley R.

TOOL INTRO – REALITY CHECK

The fact is you are human. You are not perfect. You will make bad decisions. GOGI realizes and accepts that humans make poor decisions. However, GOGI realizes that humans do not need to remain in bad decision-making mode.

If you take ten steps forward and two steps backward, you are still eight steps ahead. With GOGI, REALITY CHECK states that we focus on the GOOD and the PROGRESS rather than the poor decisions.

For as long as you are human, you may make bad decisions, but your ability to get back on track quickly is your REALITY CHECK.

Reality Check is a great tool for me to use when I find myself relapsing into old destructive behaviors. It helps me realize that there will be times when I will make mistakes; that no one is perfect. However, Reality Check allows me to look at my mistakes without the feeling of failure. It also helps me to realize that the mistakes that I do make will not dictate my level of success. With Reality Check, I will not be discouraged when I stumble and fall. I will simply get up, dust myself off, and start moving forward once again.

Bihn N.

HOW TO USE – REALITY CHECK

You can use REALITY CHECK with others and with yourself. Instead of focusing on the bad decisions, you focus on the improvements.

Focus on the positive. This will make it easier to overcome the disappointment that naturally comes when we make bad decisions.

Just say to yourself, "Ten steps forward and two steps back is still eight steps ahead." This will remind you that you are moving forward and give you your REALITY CHECK.

I ENJOY & LOVE THIS TOOL CAUSE I KNOW THAT I CAN BE doING A GOOD & POSITIVE PROGRAM AND doING WHAT I NEED TO do, AND WHEN I do HAVE A SET BACK IT IS OK, BECAUSE THIS TOOL HELPS YOU REALIZE THAT BACKSLIdING A LITTLE doES NOT HINDER YOUR POSITIVE PROGRAM THAT YOU HAVE BEEN doING. YOUR STILL AHEAD AND YOU CAN GET BACK ON TRACK AND MOVE PAST THE SET BACK, LIKE THE TOOL SAYS (TEN STEPS FORWARD & TWO STEPS BACK) I AM STILL EIGHT STEPS AHEAD.

Michael V.

ACTIVITY – REALITY CHECK

In small groups, in pairs, or alone, this activity will give you the power you need to make more positive decisions.

1. List or state five things you have done which are positive.
2. Now state one thing you have done recently, which was negative.
3. Repeat by listing or stating the five things or five additional things you have done in the past which are positive.
4. Write or say this statement, "Ten steps forward and two steps back is still eight steps ahead. My REALITY CHECK is that I am still moving in the right direction."

This activity will encourage all group members to be more compassionate towards themselves and others.

Claiming responsibility is used in GOGI as a powerful tool in the here and now that will help you shape your future. Using it will show that it is up to yourself and only yourself to determine what your actions and reactions will be. The only person who can control your thoughts and actions is yourself.

Robert D.

REVIEW – REALITY CHECK

With REALITY CHECK, you can realize you are human, but you do not need to be defined by poor choices. You can be defined by your successes, instead.

REALITY CHECK acknowledges that you are human, you are not perfect, and that there is no reason why you can't make the perfect decision right now.

REALITY CHECK gives you the 10 and 2 rule. Remember it. It will keep you safe from slipping down that slope toward yet-another rodeo ride. Ten steps forward and two steps back is still eight steps ahead. The 10 and 2 rule will come in very handy during your process of creating a positive life.

The saddest moment is when GOGI gets word that a GOGI student was released and did fine for awhile, but then, because they are embarrassed, they drop off the radar. Then, before too long we get an emotional letter from them from their jail cell. REALITY CHECK helps stop this before the rodeo ride gets out of control.

From Coach Taylor
REALITY CHECK

REALITY CHECK was one of the last tools to be added to the GOGI tool box. And, it was only added when GOGI students kept making mistakes. I would tell them to relax. They are, after all, human and prone to mistakes. I reminded them that ten steps forward and two steps back was still eight steps ahead.

The REALITY CHECK is that no one is perfect, but we can keep getting better every day. REALITY CHECK is an important tool because people sometimes give up if they make one mistake. Even if they were to make multiple mistakes, it is never too late to make the next positive decision. REALITY CHECK reminds us to make that positive decision, no matter what.

You will find great peace of mind when you permit yourself to recover from mistakes with the grace and ease that REALITY CHECK offers. There is no blame. There is no bashing. There is just getting right back up and marching toward your goal. That is a powerful individual, one who does not get taken down by their human frailties.

♡ Coach

Thoughts from Coach Leigh Carlson

You are human. You are not perfect. You may mess up. You may think, say and do things that are not positive, or not your very best. Truth is, you can be exceptional; you can be happy, sober and confident. And with REALITY CHECK you can stay on track. I use REALITY CHECK to cope with mistakes in daily life, from an error at work to slipping into old negative thinking about self or others. REALITY CHECK gets you off the slippery slope of messing up, not being good enough, or being afraid of failure, and it says, "do not give up, it is not over, get up and get moving."

REALITY CHECK shines a light on our progress and helps each of us keep our focus on what we have accomplished, what steps we have taken to improve our lives and the lives of others, and it does not let us be defeated or defeat ourselves. REALITY CHECK is not an excuse to mess up, it is recognition that we are human and will mess up; it is our very own permission to get back on track without throwing in the towel or surrendering to old behavior, beliefs, temptations or challenges.

REALITY CHECK says – TEN STEPS FORWARD AND TWO STEPS BACK IS STILL EIGHT STEPS AHEAD.

REALITY CHECK IN ACTION –

It is easy to forget all of the progress we've made when we mess up, because the poor decision seems to be what we and others focus on and we get caught in it over and over again instead of calling it what it is; a mess up, a relapse in behavior, or a backslide. We often get so caught up in the relapse of old behavior that we let it take us down. REALITY CHECK can be applied in these situations so that we do not lose our forward momentum and we do not give up.

Imagine you have been on the right path now for quite some time; you are in school, have built healthy relationships, have remained peaceful, sober, have helped others with their studies and you are a reliable friend, worker and human being. Imagine it feels like nothing can stop you, you are going to the parole board in a few weeks and things look good. Then boom, your cell gets stripped down, you get written up and do time in Ad Seg for having a cell phone. You go to board in a few weeks and you are sure this means a denial. You cannot believe you could have made such a bad choice. Are you going to let that one poor decision negate all of the progress you have made? No. CLAIM RESPONSIBILITY and move forward. You have more progress to make.

GOGI 4 Life!

Coach Carlson

Coach Carlson

GROUP QUESTIONS – REALITY CHECK

1. Why do you think many people give up when they make one mistake?
2. Why do you think REALITY CHECK is a good tool for these people?
3. How might you use REALITY CHECK as a GOGI tool?
4. How is having a reality check different from using the GOGI TOOL called REALITY CHECK?
5. What does eight steps ahead mean to you?

when I explain to friends or homeboys about GogI, I always got a cold stare, but when they ask me why am I always smiling or humble. I explain the 12 tools of GogI and how it have helped me deal with certain situations in my life, I contribute to GogI, my time, I explain to everyone that, we all need someone to encourage us to make better decisions in our life

Peer Coach Donivan

WEEKLY STUDY GUIDE

(Facilitator, when possible, please make a copy of this guide and distribute at the beginning of your meeting. With this guide, students can make certain they are learning the important concepts of this week's tool)

Today's date______________________________

My name________________________________

Please answer all questions. Please feel free to look in your book for the answers, discuss with fellow students, or ask your facilitator.

1) In what SECTION OF TOOLS does this tool belong? ______________________________

   ____

2) What MONTH OF THE YEAR is dedicated to the study of this tool? ____________________

3) What WEEKS OF THE YEAR are dedicated to the study of this tool? ____________________

   ____

4) What are the KEY WORDS for this tool?

   ____

   ____

5) What is the STATEMENT OF OWNERSHIP for this tool? ______________________________

____

____

____

____

____

____

6) Think about a time in your life, either past, present, or future, when this tool might be useful to you. How might you use this tool? __________

____

____

____

____

____

____

____

____

STATEMENT OF OWNERSHIP
ULTIMATE FREEDOM

ULTIMATE FREEDOM

I create ULTIMATE FREEDOM for myself when I live THE GOGI WAY. Through my service, I have ULTIMATE FREEDOM.

Repeat this week's statement of ownership as often as possible. Before you get out of bed, before your meals, during a break, and before sleeping. Write this statement for added emphasis. Your weekly statement of ownership reinforces this week's tool.

MY GOGI TOOL

ULTIMATE FREEDOM

Weeks to study ULTIMATE FREEDOM are:

4th Week of March

4th Week of June

4th Week of September

4th Week of December

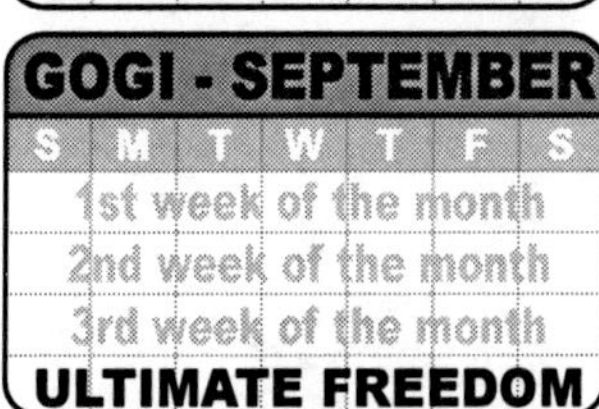

KEY WORDS
ULTIMATE FREEDOM

BEING FREE IS UP TO ME

Living a life of service
gives me
ULTIMATE FREEDOM.

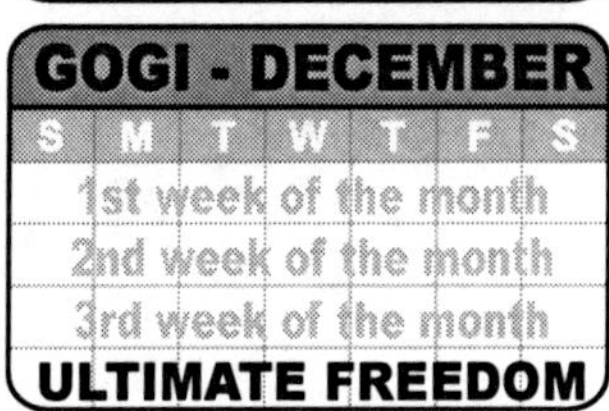

Getting Out by Going In • P.O. Box 88969 • Los Angeles, CA 90009
www.gettingoutbygoingin.org

OBJECTIVE – ULTIMATE FREEDOM

Your goal this week is to practice creating freedom in your life by doing good things, even when no one is looking.

ULTIMATE FREEDOM is this week's tool; and you can be the boss of your level of freedom when you practice ULTIMATE FREEDOM each day.

Art by Xavier H.

AGENDA – ULTIMATE FREEDOM

Here is the outline for this week's 90-minute GOGI class/group:

1. Call Your Meeting to Order (1 min)
2. Reading of your GOGI Tools (1 min)
3. Check-in/Recap of Last Week
   A very short recap (10 mins)
4. Check GOGI national calendar
   What is the tool of this week? (1 min)
5. Reading and Activity
   For this tool from this chapter (30 mins)
6. Group Discussions
   Found in this chapter (40-50 mins)
7. Closing Thoughts (1 min)
8. Your GOGI Pledge & Close of Meeting (5 mins)

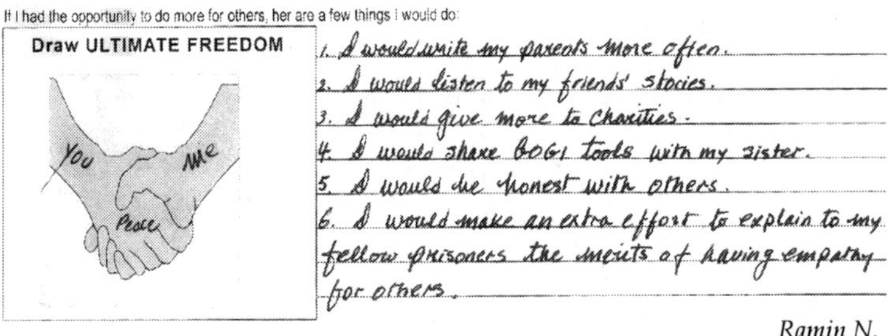

If I had the opportunity to do more for others, her are a few things I would do:

Draw ULTIMATE FREEDOM

You

Me

Peace

1. I would write my parents more often.
2. I would listen to my friends' stories.
3. I would give more to charities.
4. I would share GOGI tools with my sister.
5. I would be honest with others.
6. I would make an extra effort to explain to my fellow prisoners the merits of having empathy for others.

Ramin N.

TOOL INTRO – ULTIMATE FREEDOM

ULTIMATE FREEDOM is a feeling inside you that no one and no situation can take away. ULTIMATE FREEDOM is also something you are in charge of creating for yourself. And, ULTIMATE FREEDOM is available for everyone, not just a few people who have something you do not.

ULTIMATE FREEDOM is the freedom that comes when you decide to live your life in service of others. When you choose to live your life for something more than your own desires and needs, you begin to feel the little sparks of ULTIMATE FREEDOM.

With all my respect, coach, I just dont want a certificate I want to be more, a gogi teacher. I want to learn from the best of GOGI and help people out from in there. To be a winner, successful and change there enviroment mind of Cummunal. I want to do that.

Ill do anything to go forward. If I change, I know people could change. Now I have the book of How to gogi, this is my next level by learning how to learn.

Im preparin my self at this moment, by useing the twelves tools of gogi. I want to do more. but the staff wants me too teach GOGI in another institution because they helpin me, and they want me to teach more than 200 inmate than 10 inmates. So at this moment Im teachin the tewelve Steps of gogi for now. Until I get tranfer to another Insti, Im willin to participate on bein a coach and many more.

Leo P.

HOW TO USE – ULTIMATE FREEDOM

You can use the tool ULTIMATE FREEDOM at any time. All you need to do is focus your attention on being of service and helping to make a situation better.

You use ULTIMATE FREEDOM by moving into a POSITIVE ACTION that helps someone else. When you practice this way of living long enough, you may find yourself beginning to live in ULTIMATE FREEDOM every day, and your life will be truly, forever, ultimately happy.

I'm just so excited about all that is happening to me, I'm feeling myself Transforming into this worrier of GOGI, For your spirit, your book of tools Has resurrected a new and improved spirit herein me. Last month I lost my Baby brother , to cancer, which when i first received the news, I was About to sink into a serious state of depression, but sat down right on top Of the GOGI, book of tools, and instantly a cool and calm feeling came over Me, and my body became relax'd, I closed me eye's, fell into a deep sleep And when I awakend, the book was still tightly clench'd in my hand, and I Began to read "THE BOSS OF MY BRAIN " taking deep belly breathing inbetween Then pausing for awhile longer than the five second lightswitch, and "WOW" Positive thoughts just bloom'd and blossom'd all through my mind, producing Positive word's, which were written down and used therein my class, giving Everyone energy from, and for positive actions, That sadness, feeling of Depression triggered by my brothers passing, was no more, I was able to Let Go, FOR-GIVE, And I'm ready to give you my full attention, and service, I can only thank our creator for His, blessing me with this GOGI,connection Inwhich HE, has used you, to resurrect me, and put me to work, and it feels Absolutely wonderful to be bless'd with a never ending job, just as that Popular song goes "I'm Happy" (SMILE) I truly am happy.

* Coach, Once again I thank you for you time, efforts and support,

May you, and all involved in GOGI, Be bless'd, including family and Friends too, Be bless'd in all they do.

Gregory H.

ACTIVITY – ULTIMATE FREEDOM

You will probably find this activity very rewarding. Ask the group members what they would do in each situation. After they state what they would do, ask them how it would make them feel to do that action.

1. An old man is putting gas in his car. He turns and trips over the gas hose. What do you do? How does it feel to do this?
2. A girl is turning to walk down an alley you know is dangerous and she does not look like she knows where she is going. What do you do? How does it feel to do this?
3. A little kid is lost in the store and he is crying. You do not see his mother or father, or anyone around. What do you do? How do you feel about this?
4. You find a purse on the side of the road. The wallet is there with business cards and a phone number. What do you do? How do you feel?
5. You have the ability and opportunity to help someone in need acquire something; food, transportation, clothing, etc. They will never know it was you that assisted them, but you give what you can. How does it feel to do this?

Have the group consider these and other scenarios and discuss how it feels to be of service to others.

REVIEW – ULTIMATE FREEDOM

ULTIMATE FREEDOM is a tool, but it is also a way of gaining the only form of freedom that can never be taken away. This is because ULTIMATE FREEDOM is created from inside you and it is yours to keep for as long as you like. ULTIMATE FREEDOM is a result of your ability to use the GOGI Tools to help others so that you can feel the power that comes from being of service.

ULTIMATE FREEDOM is achieved in little moments of service, but if you do enough of these little moments each day, you will find your life keeps getting better and better. You will want to be of more service, because your life begins to be so powerfully positive.

From Coach Taylor
ULTIMATE FREEDOM

ULTIMATE FREEDOM was the tool that resulted from the use of all the other tools. When the GOGI students used the other tools, they found it natural to live their lives in service of others. That is why GOGI students smile more than most people, why they don't get bothered by irritating people, why they don't get upset with long lines, or disgruntled supervisors. GOGI people understand that being of service to others is often done by reacting peacefully to the daily irritations that get some people really wound up. GOGI people are peaceful people, because they live in service of others and they live an ULTIMATE FREEDOM that very few people can understand.

♡ Coach

NOW HERE I SERVE OTHER HAS A TUTOR IN GED AND A FACILITATOR IN GOGI. ALSO I ORGANIZE OTHER EVENTS IN SPANISH HELPING PEOPLE OF LATIN CULTURE PARTICIPATE. EVERY DAY I ORGANIZE THE SMALL LIBRARY AND THRU THESE DIFFERENT ACTIVITIES I FIND ULTIMATE FREEDOM AND SATISFACTION.

Michael J.

Thoughts from Coach Leigh Carlson

When something is difficult or challenging, I say to myself – BEING FREE IS UP TO ME. This gets me out of my own way and into being of service. GOGI has put a light on my ability to get out of my own prison, and has given me the willingness to stop limiting myself. As a result of understanding that it is up to me, I was able to use the GOGI TOOLS to rebuild my life and live my life in ULTIMATE FREEDOM – in service to others. There is no greater joy and no greater way to heal.

ULTIMATE FREEDOM IN ACTION —

I worked with men in GOGI's Leadership Training at Men's Central jail in Los Angeles for nearly three years. In my time there the majority of our GOGI students faced long sentences. Every single one of them held their heads high and said that they would take GOGI with them; that they will choose their path and it will be positive. They are choosing ULTIMATE FREEDOM. That path is not easy in prison; it is the GOGI Way. You see; you are the mentors and the teachers. You are the coaches we need to learn, share and live the GOGI Way. GOGI knows that the only true lasting internal peace that no one, nowhere can ever take away comes through service to others. BEING FREE IS UP TO ME – Being of service sets me internally free. No matter where you wake up, you can have internal peace and freedom through service to others.

GOGI 4 Life!

Coach Carlson

Coach Carlson

GROUP QUESTIONS – ULTIMATE FREEDOM

1. Why do you think some people believe freedom is never going to be theirs to enjoy?

2. When you think about times that you helped someone else, did you enjoy the feeling? Please explain.

3. Why does GOGI state that ULTIMATE FREEDOM is the only kind of freedom that can never be taken away?

4. What is the difference between physical freedom and ULTIMATE FREEDOM?

Draw ULTIMATE FREEDOM

From Coach Taylor
ULTIMATE FREEDOM

Being willing to participate in the development of GOGI has set me free from the prison I had created in my own mind. The gratitude I now show is by sharing these tools with anyone who is seeking their own internal freedom. This is my ULTIMATE FREEDOM, the sharing of what has been given to me.

♡ Coach

GOGI Girls FCI Dublin

WEEKLY STUDY GUIDE

(Facilitator, when possible, please make a copy of this guide and distribute at the beginning of your meeting. With this guide, students can make certain they are learning the important concepts of this week's tool)

Today's date______________________________

My name_________________________________

Please answer all questions. Please feel free to look in your book for the answers, discuss with fellow students, or ask your facilitator.

1) In what SECTION OF TOOLS does this tool belong? ______________________________

____

2) What MONTH OF THE YEAR is dedicated to the study of this tool? ____________________

3) What WEEKS OF THE YEAR are dedicated to the study of this tool? ____________________

____

4) What are the KEY WORDS for this tool?

____

____

5) What is the STATEMENT OF OWNERSHIP for this tool? ______________________

____

____

____

____

____

____

6) Think about a time in your life, either past, present, or future, when this tool might be useful to you. How might you use this tool? ________

____

____

____

____

____

____

____

____

DO YOU KNOW YOUR GOGI?

Can you answer the following questions?

What are the FOUR SECTIONS OF GOGI TOOLS that prisoners created?

TOOLS OF THE BODY
TOOLS OF CHOICE
TOOLS OF MOVING FORWARD
TOOLS OF CREATION

What are the names of each of the GOGI TOOLS FOR POSITIVE DECISION MAKING that prisoners created?

BOSS OF MY BRAIN
BELLY BREATHING
FIVE SECOND LIGHTSWITCH
POSITIVE THOUGHTS
POSITIVE WORDS
POSITIVE ACTIONS
CLAIM RESPONSIBILITY
LET GO
FOR--GIVE
WHAT IF
REALITY CHECK
ULTIMATE FREEDOM

DO YOU KNOW YOUR GOGI?

What are the KEY WORDS prisoners created?

BOSS OF MY BRAIN – Smart Part, Emotional Part, Old Habit Part. Which one is in charge?

BELLY BREATHING – Hand on stomach. Hand on chest. Which one is moving?

FIVE SECOND LIGHTSWITCH – Old thought? I have a new action. By the count of five, I get to my new action.

POSITIVE THOUGHTS – Is it Powerful? Productive? Positive?

POSITIVE WORDS – Is it Powerful? Productive? Positive?

POSITIVE ACTIONS – Is it Powerful? Productive? Positive?

CLAIM RESPONSIBILITY – I own today. I ask myself, "Am I proud of this choice?"

LET GO – hand / squash / toss

FOR--GIVE – For me to give I must be safe from harm.

WHAT IF – What if I am not my past?

REALITY CHECK – Ten steps forward and two steps back is still eight steps ahead.

ULTIMATE FREEDOM – Being free is up to me.

DO YOU KNOW YOUR GOGI?

What is the GOGI CALENDAR created by prisoners?
The GOGI Calendar assigns one tool for each week of the year.

Why do all students study the same tool at the same time?
The GOGI Calendar unites GOGI studies around the world so no one will ever study GOGI alone.

Why did prisoners ask that GOGI have an OFFICIAL MEETING FORMAT and a MINI MEETING FORMAT?
Prisoners created the OFFICIAL MEETING FORMAT and the MINI MEETING FORMAT so they could unite the GOGI family into a positive community. The MINI MEETING can be used if meeting time is limited.

Why did prisoners create the GOGI pledge?
Prisoners created the GOGI pledge to express their verbal commitment to use the tools and remain free by being of service.

DO YOU KNOW YOUR GOGI?

The GOGI Pledge
Can you say it from memory?

May our commitment
To the study of GOGI
Grant us the joy
Of giving and receiving
So that our inner freedom
May be of maximum service
To those we love
And infinite others

Who created GOGI?
GOGI was created by PRISONERS for PRISONERS.

Do you know that anyone may hold a GOGI meeting?
GOGI meetings can be held when two or more people gather to study GOGI and follow the official meeting format.

If asked, could you pick a favorite tool and describe how you would use it?

CLASS DISCUSSION AND OPTIONAL WRITING ASSIGNMENTS

You now have the GOGI TOOLS FOR POSITIVE DECISION MAKING to help you make more positive decisions. Please take a moment to write a little something about each of your new tools.

1. BOSS OF MY BRAIN tells me that I have a SMART PART, EMOTIONAL PART and OLD HABIT PART. Here is what I think about BOSS OF MY BRAIN.

2. BELLY BREATHING has me check to make sure my belly is moving when I breathe. This is important for me, because:

3. The GOGI TOOL FIVE SECOND LIGHTSWITCH lets me swap old thoughts with a new action. Here is how I use FIVE SECOND LIGHTSWITCH.

4. POSITIVE THOUGHTS are mine to create. Here are some of my favorite POSITIVE THOUGHTS.

5. POSITIVE WORDS are mine to choose. Here are some of my favorite POSITIVE WORDS.

6. POSITIVE ACTIONS are mine to do. Here are some of my favorite POSITIVE ACTIONS.

7. The GOGI Tool CLAIM RESPONSIBILITY states I am in charge of my actions and in charge of my reactions today. This means that:

8. LET GO is something I can do with my HAND/SQUASH/TOSS. Today I can LET GO of:

9. FOR--GIVE and FOR--GIVING requires that I am safe from harm. Today I can make sure I am safe from:

10. The GOGI TOOL WHAT IF allows me to see what might happen with my decisions. My favorite WHAT IF is to:

11. I am human and humans make mistakes. For this reason, it is important for me to remember REALITY CHECK. I have been successful in the following ways:

12. My ULTIMATE FREEDOM comes when I think of doing something for someone else. Here are things I like to do for others.

13. How can your GOGI tools help you in the future?

14. If asked, how would you describe GOGI?

Will You Write Us?

Did you like this book? We want to hear how it helped you and we welcome your letters. Do you have artwork or a poem you want to give to us to share with others? Please send us your gifts of artwork, poems or pictures and we will share them with the GOGI community.

At GOGI, we enjoy receiving letters from people who study our materials. We sure would like to hear from you, too! Write us at:

The GOGI Mailroom
PO Box 88969
Los Angeles, CA 90009

Do You Want More GOGI?

This book is just one book in the family of GOGI books. You will find a list of all our books at the following website: ***www. gettingoutbygoingin.org,*** where you can buy the books and have them shipped to you or to someone else.

We offer discounts for schools and facilities when they purchase quantities for their students. We will also work with your group for fundraisers you may wish to hold.

Donations

Did you know GOGI is a non-profit organization that operates only on donations with volunteers to serve the public?

We are grateful for the donations we receive from people who send us stamps, a check or make an online donation in any amount. We are only growing because of our donors.

Adam B.

You Did It!

Daniel O.

Now What?

From Coach Taylor

A message to you from the Founder of GOGI

Now that you have completed this book, you may be asking yourself the question, "Now what?" You may have found one or more of the GOGI tools helpful. You may have found that your study in a group format brought a sense of positive community to your life. You may actually miss your weekly GOGI meetings if your group has an end date.

The good news is that more and more GOGI students are finding that when a group study ends, their GOGI life just begins. More and more GOGI students are coming to realize that the use of the tools can continue, and most of all, that they can build a community that is positive by continuing to meet with group members, or other individuals, to meet and discuss and apply the GOGI TOOLS FOR POSITIVE DECISION MAKING.

While GOGI Groups started by people from different areas coming together to meet, an increasing number of GOGI Groups are happening inside homes, inside housing units, inside cells. Keeping the study small and localized has proven to be even more powerful than having to relocate, move, shift or travel to a

GOGI meeting. If that sounds strange, that is only because it is not yet familiar. GOGI meetings are best when conducted in small groups of people who live close to each other and have daily contact with each other.

If you want to continue with GOGI, you do not need anything more than a GOGI book and the desire to include GOGI tools into your daily POSITIVE THOUGHTS, POSITIVE WORDS, and POSITIVE ACTIONS.

Look at it this way. Your life is filled with choices you make. You choose who to say hello to in the morning. You choose who to listen to during the day. You choose who you stand near, make eye contact with and what you discuss. Why not choose to add a little GOGI into your daily conversation?

Most people are pretty bored with life. Most people say the same things today that they said yesterday. Most people want something new and different to show up for their eyes and ears to experience. What if you simply said the words I am BOSS OF MY BRAIN today? The other person would say, "What on earth are you talking about?" And with that one sentence, you have introduced someone to your desired conversation.

You see, you are not as trapped or stuck as you may have believed. And you are in no way as limited as you believe yourself to be. Your current limits have been assumed by you as reality because that is what you see day in and day out. You have accepted the current limits because you did not apply tools to create an alternative. But with even the smallest shift, with starting one conversation about a GOGI tool, you may begin to see that you have unlimited control of your life's direction.

Start a little GOGI weekly meeting with some friends instead of sitting down to watch TV. Just ask if they will join you in a book reading. Invite someone who does not know how to read to sit with you and you explain what each letter sounds like. All the while they will be learning their GOGI tools.

Now what? I ask you that question. You have a beautiful tool box. Will you close it up and put it in a locker? Or will you start using it, sharing it, and living The GOGI Way?

♡ Coach

A GOGI Challenge

My name is Herbert "Hube" Smith and if there's anyone who doubts that GOGI works, here is my challenge: When I first challenged the GOGI TOOL — FIVE SECOND LIGHTSWITCH, I couldn't say a complete sentence without using profanity so I felt my language was a worthy opponent to test this GOGI TOOL. To me, FIVE SECOND LIGHTSWITCH is simple: Old Thought. New Action. Here is how I explain it. Once you catch yourself with the old thought, by the count of 5, do a pre-planned NEW ACTION.
Here is how I used the GOGI TOOL FIVE SECOND LIGHTSWITCH in my GOGI CHALLENGE. When I'd be talking to someone and I'd cuss, I'd start to count and snap my fingers twice. After a few days I'd snap my fingers before the cuss words would come out. Slowly but surely, I stopped snapping my fingers. And, I was choosing more POSITIVE WORDS to get an idea across.

People asked me what I was doing and I explained it. To my amazement I noticed others snapping their fingers too. I rarely cuss now and it's all due to a simple challenge to prove that the GOGI Tools work. Here's a very simple truth. I realized that by doing a simple challenge, I took the first step to a better life!

If I can be GOGI, then anyone can. GOGI 4 LIFE
Your GOGI brother,

Herbert "Hube" Smith

SEND US YOUR GOGI CHALLENGE!

SECTION FIVE:

GOGI TESTIMONIALS

Coach Lucero

GOGI STUDENT TESTIMONIAL

How exciting to share my story with the world! My name is Coach Lucero. This wonderful journey started with me sitting in the same place as most of you reading this. I started GOGI while incarcerated. What caught my attention with GOGI was learning that I could truly change my thought process with something so simple like the tool BOSS OF MY BRAIN. Then learning that I could focus again using BELLY BREATHING, I was hooked.

Well about 2 weeks before the GOGI graduation I was transferred to a different facility, and I was lost. I knew I needed GOGI. So I wrote to Coach Taylor and my family ordered me the GOGI 12-week certification program. I got a new HOW TO GOGI book and studied, finished my workbook and began teaching GOGI at the facility where I was. I learned more than I taught, and the success with GOGI and the women made me want to strive to become better. I wanted these women to grow as I have grown, learn what I have learned, feel and notice the change I became. GOGI taught me who I always wanted to be, and I am proof that the constant application of the GOGI tools works.

After 3 graduating classes, I decided to get my Coach certification. I followed all of the levels of study in the HOW TO GOGI book and did my special assignment. I was transferred to another facility where they had a GOGI campus, and I helped with peer coaching as I worked toward coach status. I met the most beautiful and amazing women there and they all live the GOGI way together, I was honored to be a part of such a wonderful group of women.

I spent a total of 26 months incarcerated that time. So when I paroled, I was ready to bring GOGI into the community. I am still working towards that goal. I live the GOGI way and have been blessed with a wonderful kind of freedom, called ULTIMATE FREEDOM. Helping others, and creating this life for myself, I won't look back. I am going only one way and that's forward.

I have a great job, my family and my life back. I am volunteering in the GOGI mailroom, and working on getting GOGI at the Parole office as an alternative to incarceration. I am in constant contact with Coach Taylor, Coach Carlson, Coach Bristow, and many others in my GOGI family. I am living proof that this program works. I have been sober 3 years and I owe my success to GOGI. I encourage you to keep studying and if you have any questions, I promise you that if you write to GOGI they will always answer you back!!! I encourage you to start your own GOGI groups and start peer coaching. It's so simple, and I promise you that if you live the GOGI way, your life will only become better each and every day. Thank you to GOGI for all of your support through this journey. If it wasn't for you and believing in us, I seriously don't know where I would be. Always stay POSITIVE, POWERFUL, and PRODUCTIVE!

Love, Coach Lucero

Testimonial from COACH STRONGER

My name is Melanie. I am 53 years old and have been in and out of jails and institutions for the last 25 years of my life. In those 25 years I let two things control my life, drugs and my relationships. I have been in several programs through out the years, which were in-patient and outpatient, and nothing seemed to work for me.

Then, one lucky day, I was moved to a housing unit at the Wasatch County Jail called "GOGI Campus." In this housing unit there were women who were reading the HOW TO GOGI book. I started reading, wondering why everyone in this part of the jail was so happy. The first thing that I read in the GOGI book that caught my eye was that it said that anyone can change if they truly have a desire to change, but it usually has to be a matter of life or death. For me it was a matter of life or death because if I did not change, I was going to die on the streets from my addiction or die behind the prison walls.

For the first time in my life I made a conscious decision to put my whole heart into this "program" called GOGI. I learned and then came to love the GOGI TOOLS FOR POSITIVE DECISION MAKING. And I especially love that today I am BOSS OF MY BRAIN.

My GOGI tools have become my new, positive and automatic habit that I use daily. My favorite is BELLY BREATHING, which I still use in all negative situations. Today I CLAIM RESPONSIBILITY for my actions and reactions. And I have learned to LET GO of things that used to bother me. I use FOR--GIVE as a tool so I can give back to others. And I have set boundaries where and when needed.

I want people to know that everyday we can be in a battlefield with our minds and that there is a way to win this war that goes on in our heads. We can win this war Getting Out by Going Inward.

I may not be where I want to be, but I thank God every day that I am not where I used to be. I thank God I have the GOGI TOOLS FOR POSITIVE DECISION MAKING to use for all my challenges. I thank my GOGI Sisters of GOGI Campus and the sacrifices of all the GOGI volunteers.

GOGI 4 Life,
Melanie Evans Stringer
AKA Coach Stronger

Words from GOGI GIRL SHANNON SCHUMAKER

When I was addicted to methamphetamine and was making the decision to get high; I was not the BOSS OF MY BRAIN. I have found that when I am the BOSS OF MY BRAIN I no longer make decisions that I might later regret. When I make a decision using the SMART PART of my brain, my thoughts and actions are thought out, which means that I am not making a decision from the EMOTIONAL PART of my brain, such as a decision made out of anger. And, because I am the BOSS OF MY BRAIN, I no longer make my decisions from the OLD HABIT PART of my brain, which resulted in a cycle of bad decisions and addiction.

In the past when a situation arose I would have just made a snap decision without thinking. I have to remind myself that BELLY BREATHING will allow me the chance to calm down and think about the situation at hand, and find a way to make it a better situation.

When I feel like I am getting stressed, I simply put one hand on my belly and that is just enough of a reminder and I get back to BELLY BREATHING and making the next positive decision.

To say that I never have thoughts of using drugs again or other negative thoughts that I struggle with would be a lie, but I now know I no longer have to act on these OLD HABIT thoughts. I can diffuse these thoughts using the FIVE SECOND LIGHTSWITCH. What I have found to work for me is to just think about five different things I have done to make my life better, and ask myself, if I were to act on these OLD HABIT thoughts, what would be the result? Pretty simple choice for me to take a POSITIVE ACTION.

Because I choose to make a conscious effort to turn a negative thought into Positive Thoughts, I am a happier, more powerful and positive person. I never would have believed that thoughts could play such a big part in how you feel about yourself. If you have negative thoughts in general, your thoughts about yourself are negative. If they are positive, you will see yourself in a positive light. Working with the homeless in the Skid Row community in Los Angeles, which is part of my job, there are many struggles and challenges for each individual. When I am able to maintain POSITIVE THOUGHTS, I am of greater service to the Skid Row community, because I am an example of positive possibilities.

I have learned that when you change your thoughts to POSITIVE THOUGHTS, your words just somehow follow to be the same. I can say POSITIVE WORDS that reinforce my continued success in my recovery. I know that drugs can always be a threat that could sneak up at any time and I have to be aware of the triggers. I need to be sure to use POSITIVE WORDS to not only empower myself, but others as well.

POSITIVE ACTIONS come from having POSITIVE THOUGHTS and POSITIVE WORDS. Today I can be proud of my actions. I no longer have to worry about the consequences that will come from my actions, because my actions are no longer harming or hurtful. Today my actions are POSITIVE, PRODUCTIVE, and POWERFUL, and more importantly they are now helpful to others.

There are so many things in my life that I have no control over, and at any time I can just choose to LET GO of them. Why am I going to let little irritants take up space in my head, when in reality, is it really going to matter a day from now? Using LET GO on a daily basis allows me to positively move forward with my day and get beyond stressful situations that may hinder my productivity.

To use the tool FOR--GIVE / FOR-GIVING, I needed to be a safe distance from my 15-year methamphetamine addiction. Once I was sober and safe, I was able to forgive myself for feeling like I had wasted years of my life in addiction. Being safe from the daily addiction, I use the tool FOR--GIVE to give back to community members with similar struggles.

For me my WHAT IF became my reality. WHAT IF I had not changed my life? WHAT IF I had not taken opportunities available to me? WHAT IF I had not seen the value of my life and my self-worth and asked myself? WHAT IF I am not my past? With this tool, I was able to ask myself WHAT IF I commit a year to my rehabilitation and join the Los Angeles Mission / Anne Douglas Center Program? WHAT IF I go back to school and work with the homeless community? WHAT IF? Now my WHAT IF is my reality.

I have made so much progress! I am drug free today for six years, and even when I make mistakes REALITY CHECK says that those decisions do not define me, nor will they erase the progress I have made and all of the good I have done for others and myself. I am still moving forward.

When I was in my addiction my whole life revolved around meth; my thoughts, words, and actions. Now that I am free from my addiction, I am living my ULTIMATE FREEDOM by pursuing a degree in Community Economic Planning and Development so that I can create programs to help with workforce development, treatment and education, as well as help people acquire housing.

CPSIA information can be obtained
at www.ICGtesting.com
Printed in the USA
FSOW02n0111300717
36810FS